Addition & Subtraction Drills

Grades 1-3

Written by Nancy Wilson
Illustrated by S&S Learning Materials

ISBN 1-55035-753-0
Copyright 2004
Revised September 2006
All Rights Reserved * Printed in Canada

Published in the United States by:
On The Mark Press
3909 Witmer Road PMB 175
Niagara Falls, New York
14305
www.onthemarkpress.com

Published in Canada by:
S&S Learning Materials
15 Dairy Avenue
Napanee, Ontario
K7R 1M4
www.sslearning.com

Other Workbooks

This series of books for grades 1 to 3 was created to strengthen a variety of skills through practice, and to aid in developing a solid understanding of the skills taught in the primary grades.

Build Their Skills in ....

Sentence Writing
Numeration
Addition
Subtraction
Phonics
Capitalization & Punctuation
Reading for Meaning
Story Writing
Handwriting Manuscript
Handwriting Cursive

Addition Drill Work Sheets

OTM-1131 • SSK1-31 Addition & Subtraction Drills

Name: _____

Adding with Zero

6 + 0 *6*	7 + 0 *7*	1 + 0 *1*	3 + 0 *3*	4 + 0 *4*
8 + 0 *8*	2 + 0 *2*	5 + 0 *5*	0 + 0 *0*	7 + 0 *7*
1 + 0 *1*	4 + 0 *4*	9 + 0 *9*	6 + 0 *6*	3 + 0 *3*
5 + 0 *5*	0 + 0 *0*	8 + 0 *8*	2 + 0 *2*	9 + 0 *9*
0 + 6 *6*	0 + 9 *9*	0 + 2 *2*	0 + 1 *0*	0 + 7 *0*
0 + 0 *0*	0 + 3 *0*	0 + 5 *0*	0 + 8 *0*	0 + 4 *0*

Number of Problems: 30   Number Correct: _____   Time to complete: ____ min.

Name: _____

Adding with One

6 + 1 *7*	8 + 1 *9*	4 + 1 *5*	9 + 1 *10*	0 + 1 *1*
7 + 1 *8*	5 + 1 *6*	3 + 1 *4*	1 + 1 *2*	2 + 1 *3*
2 + 1 *3*	8 + 1 *9*	4 + 1 *5*	3 + 1 *4*	7 + 1 *8*
1 + 1 *2*	9 + 1 *10*	5 + 1 *6*	8 + 1 *9*	6 + 1 *7*
1 + 7 *8*	1 + 3 *4*	1 + 9 *10*	1 + 5 *6*	1 + 2 *3*
1 + 8 *9*	1 + 1 *2*	1 + 6 *6*	1 + 4 *5*	1 + 0 *1*

Number of Problems: 30   Number Correct: _____   Time to complete: ____ min.

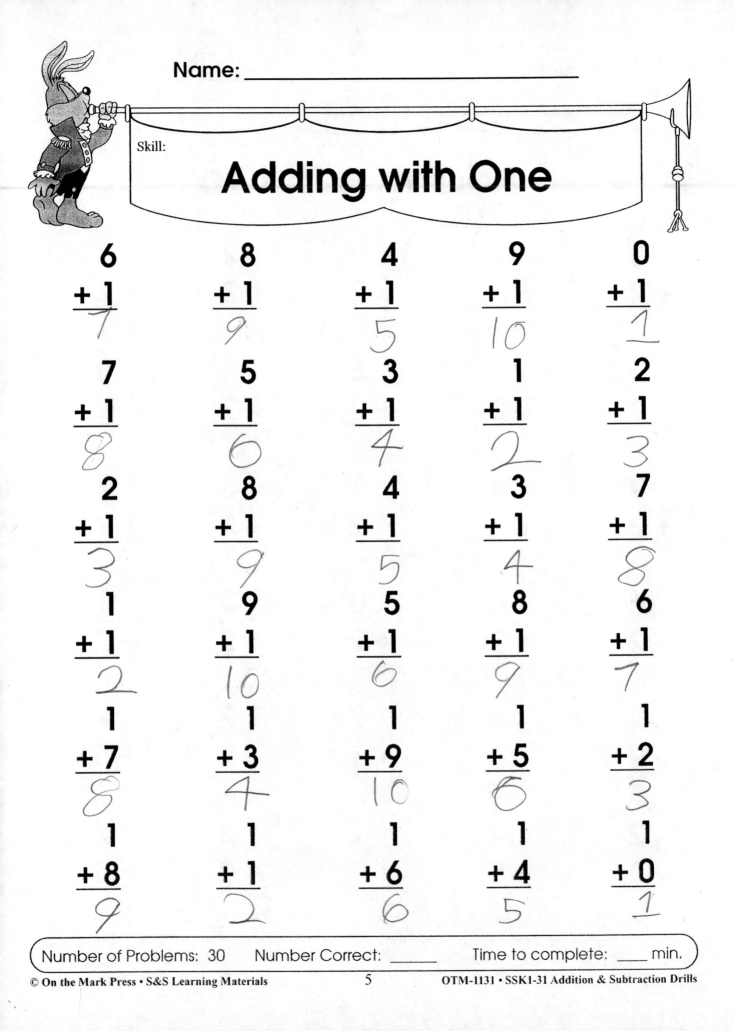

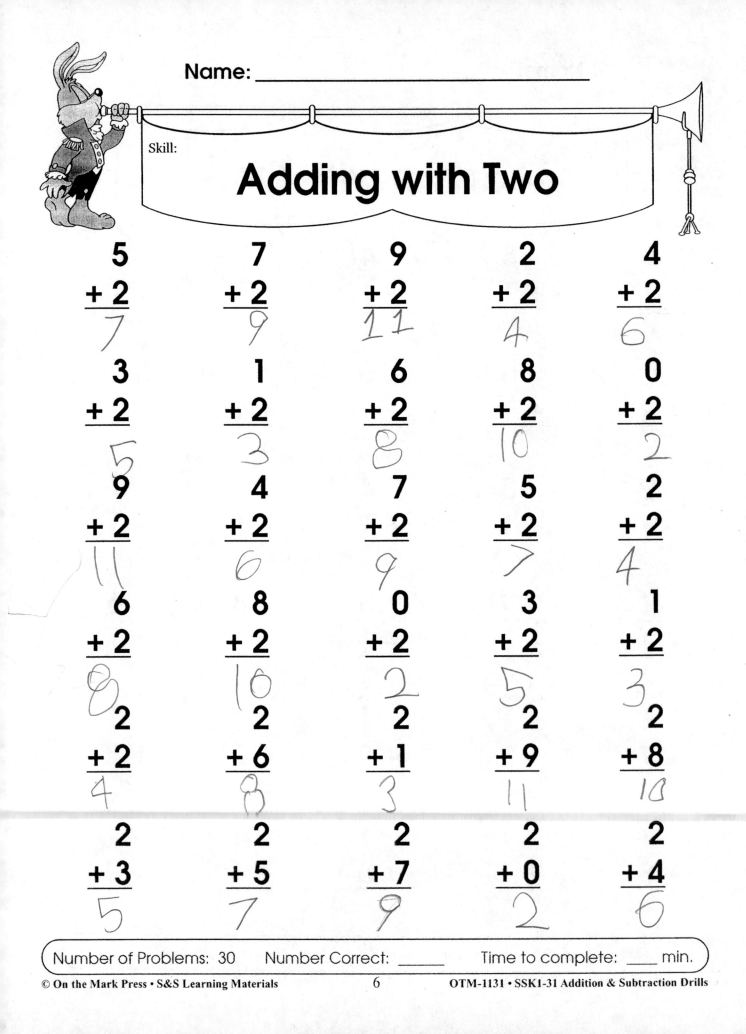

Name: _____

Skill:

Adding with Two

5 + 2 *7*	7 + 2 *9*	9 + 2 *11*	2 + 2 *4*	4 + 2 *6*
3 + 2 *5*	1 + 2 *3*	6 + 2 *8*	8 + 2 *10*	0 + 2 *2*
9 + 2 *11*	4 + 2 *6*	7 + 2 *9*	5 + 2 *7*	2 + 2 *4*
6 + 2 *8*	8 + 2 *10*	0 + 2 *2*	3 + 2 *5*	1 + 2 *3*
2 + 2 *4*	2 + 6 *8*	2 + 1 *3*	2 + 9 *11*	2 + 8 *10*
2 + 3 *5*	2 + 5 *7*	2 + 7 *9*	2 + 0 *2*	2 + 4 *6*

Number of Problems: 30   Number Correct: _____   Time to complete: ___ min.

Skill:

Adding with Three

1 + 3	7 + 3	9 + 3	5 + 3	0 + 3
2 + 3	6 + 3	4 + 3	8 + 3	3 + 3
9 + 3	1 + 3	0 + 3	7 + 3	5 + 3
3 + 3	2 + 3	8 + 3	4 + 3	6 + 3
3 + 7	3 + 2	3 + 8	3 + 4	3 + 0
3 + 1	3 + 5	3 + 9	3 + 3	3 + 6

Number of Problems: 30   Number Correct: _____   Time to complete: ____ min.

Skill:

Adding with Four

0 + 4	2 + 4	7 + 4	5 + 4	8 + 4
1 + 4	4 + 4	6 + 4	9 + 4	3 + 4
3 + 4	5 + 4	8 + 4	1 + 4	9 + 4
2 + 4	6 + 4	7 + 4	0 + 4	4 + 4
4 + 5	4 + 7	4 + 2	4 + 8	4 + 3
4 + 1	4 + 6	4 + 0	4 + 9	4 + 4

Number of Problems: 30   Number Correct: _____   Time to complete: _____ min.

Skill:

Adding with Five

6 +5	0 +5	2 +5	1 +5	5 +5
3 +5	7 +5	4 +5	9 +5	8 +5
1 +5	3 +5	8 +5	6 +5	4 +5
5 +5	9 +5	0 +5	7 +5	2 +5
5 +9	5 +5	5 +0	5 +3	5 +7
5 +6	5 +2	5 +1	5 +8	5 +4

Number of Problems: 30   Number Correct: _____   Time to complete: ____ min.

Skill:

Adding with Six

9 + 6	2 + 6	4 + 6	7 + 6	1 + 6
3 + 6	6 + 6	0 + 6	8 + 6	5 + 6
1 + 6	4 + 6	9 + 6	2 + 6	7 + 6
5 + 6	0 + 6	3 + 6	8 + 6	6 + 6
6 + 2	6 + 7	6 + 2	6 + 0	6 + 6
6 + 5	6 + 9	6 + 3	6 + 8	6 + 4

Number of Problems: 30   Number Correct: _____   Time to complete: ____ min.

Skill:

Adding with Seven

5 + 7	3 + 7	0 + 7	9 + 7	1 + 7
2 + 7	8 + 7	6 + 7	4 + 7	7 + 7
0 + 7	9 + 7	1 + 7	2 + 7	7 + 7
5 + 7	3 + 7	8 + 7	4 + 7	6 + 7
7 + 0	7 + 2	7 + 9	7 + 3	7 + 7
7 + 1	7 + 5	7 + 8	7 + 4	7 + 6

Number of Problems: 30   Number Correct: _____   Time to complete: ____ min.

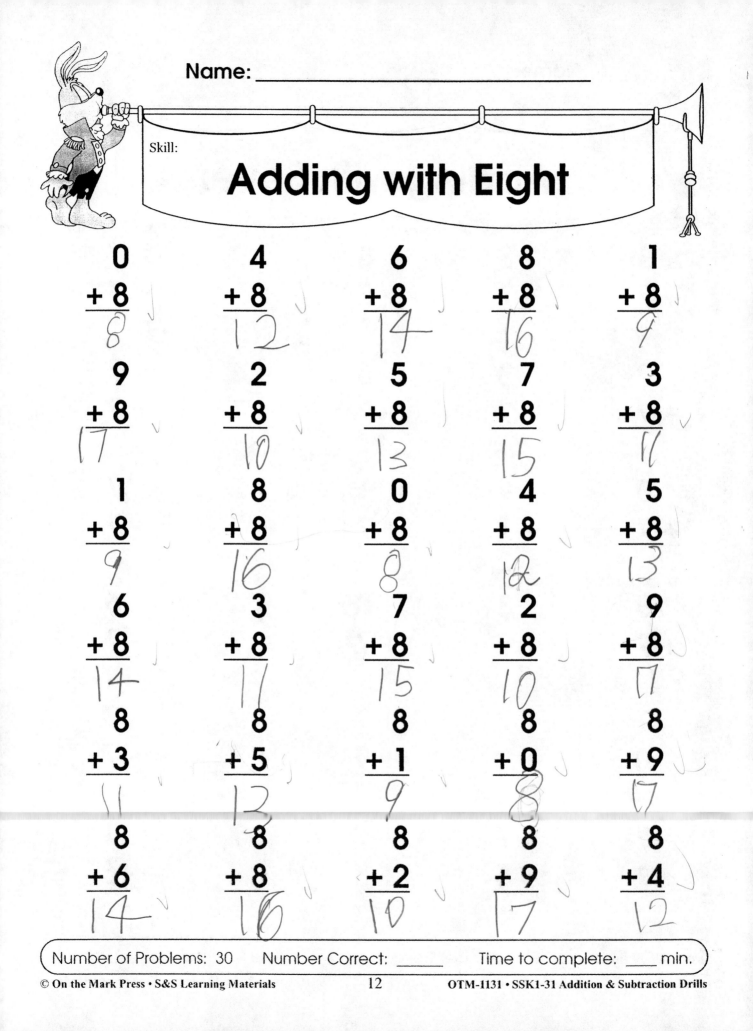

Name: _____

Skill:

Adding with Eight

0 + 8 *8*	4 + 8 *12*	6 + 8 *14*	8 + 8 *16*	1 + 8 *9*
9 + 8 *17*	2 + 8 *10*	5 + 8 *13*	7 + 8 *15*	3 + 8 *11*
1 + 8 *9*	8 + 8 *16*	0 + 8 *8*	4 + 8 *12*	5 + 8 *13*
6 + 8 *14*	3 + 8 *11*	7 + 8 *15*	2 + 8 *10*	9 + 8 *17*
8 + 3 *11*	8 + 5 *13*	8 + 1 *9*	8 + 0 *8*	8 + 9 *17*
8 + 6 *14*	8 + 8 *16*	8 + 2 *10*	8 + 9 *17*	8 + 4 *12*

Number of Problems: 30   Number Correct: _____   Time to complete: ____ min.

12   OTM-1131 • SSK1-31 Addition & Subtraction Drills

Skill:

Adding with Nine

1 + 9	5 + 9	9 + 9	6 + 9	2 + 9
7 + 9	3 + 9	8 + 9	0 + 9	4 + 9
0 + 9	4 + 9	3 + 9	7 + 9	1 + 9
9 + 9	2 + 9	5 + 9	8 + 9	6 + 9
9 + 7	9 + 1	9 + 3	9 + 9	9 + 0
9 + 2	9 + 6	9 + 4	9 + 8	9 + 5

Number of Problems: 30   Number Correct: _____   Time to complete: ____ min.

Picture Addition

Start With	Add On	All Together
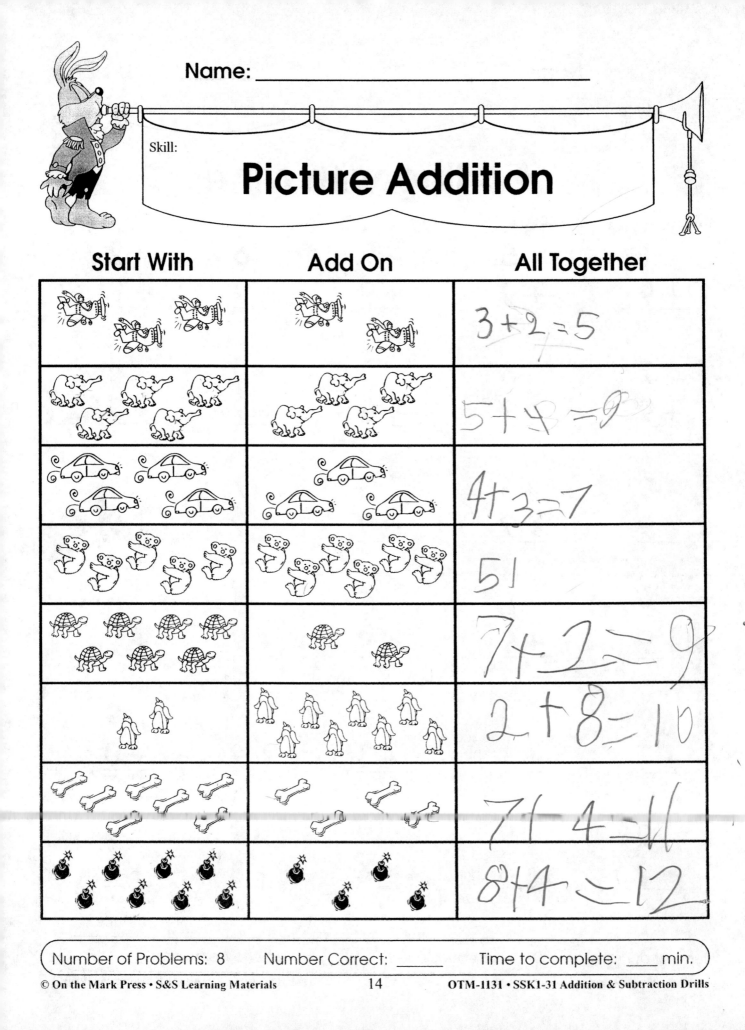		$3 + 2 = 5$
		$5 + 4 = 9$
		$4 + 3 = 7$
		51
		$7 + 2 = 9$
		$2 + 8 = 10$
		$7 + 4 = 11$
		$8 + 4 = 12$

Number of Problems: 8   Number Correct: _____   Time to complete: ____ min.

Skill:

Addition Sentences

Count the pictures in each group. Write the number on the line under each group. Then add the two groups and write the answer in the box.

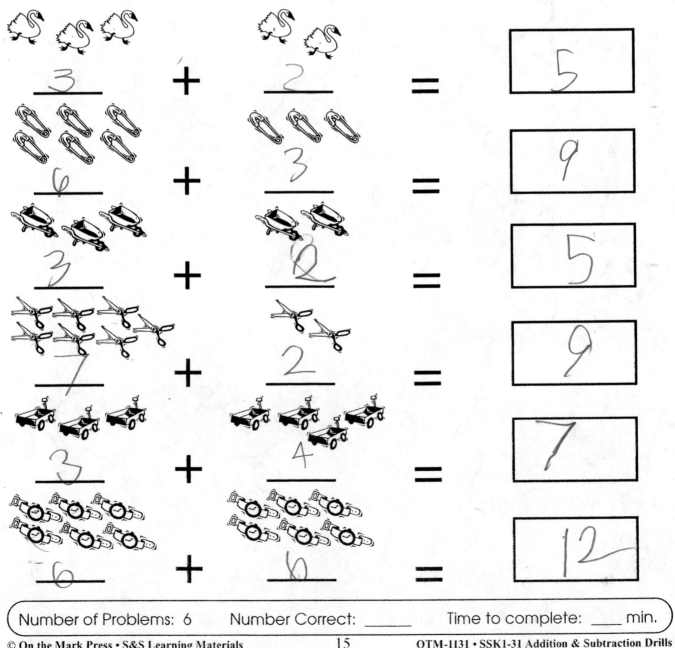

3 + 2 = 5

6 + 3 = 9

3 + 2 = 5

1 + 2 = 9

3 + 4 = 7

6 + 6 = 12

Number of Problems: 6   Number Correct: _____   Time to complete: ____ min.

© On the Mark Press • S&S Learning Materials   15   OTM-1131 • SSK1-31 Addition & Subtraction Drills

Name: _____

Skill:

Quick Addition Drill

Solve the problems inside the baby dino, then color each one.

4 +1	5 +3	2 +1	4 +3	5 +1
2 +2	5 +0	2 +3	6 +1	2 +5
1 +0	6 +3	7 +0	3 +8	2 +4

Number of Problems: 15   Number Correct: _____   Time to complete: ____ min.

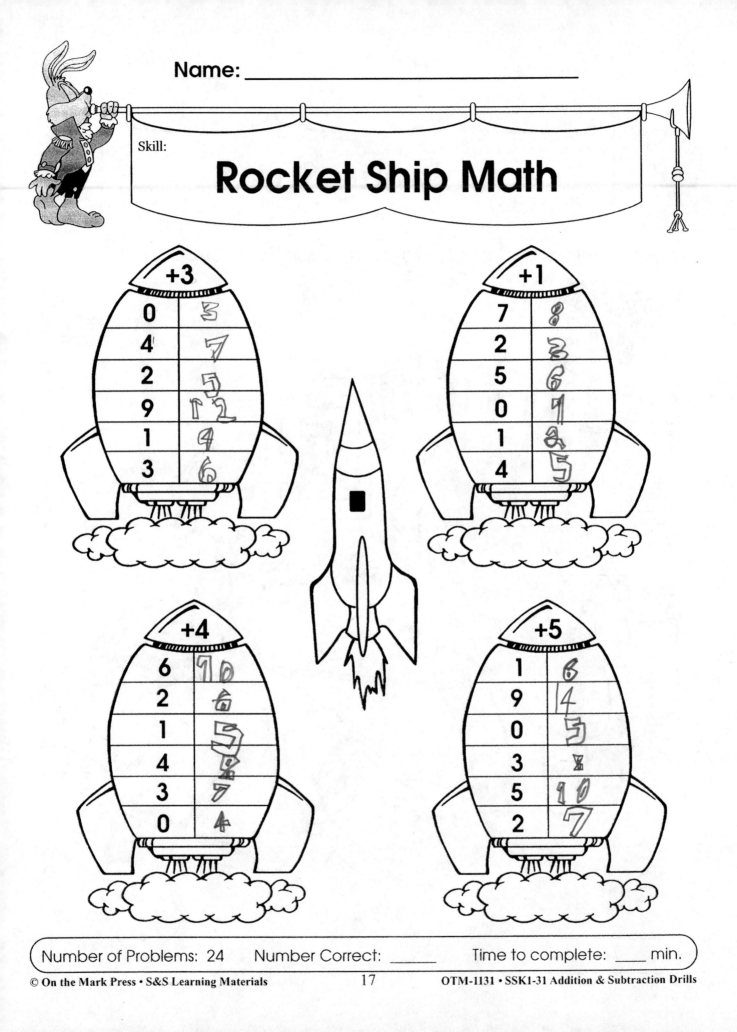

Skill:

Rocket Ship Math

+3

0	3
4	7
2	5
9	12
1	4
3	6

+1

7	8
2	3
5	6
0	1
4	5

+4

6	10
2	6
1	5
4	8
3	7
0	4

+5

1	6
9	14
0	5
3	8
5	10
2	7

Number of Problems: 24   Number Correct: _____   Time to complete: _____ min.

Skill: _____

Coloring Sums

After you have solved each problem, color the picture.

3+1 = _____

6+3 = _____

4+6 = _____

5
+3
_____

1
+4
_____

6+0 = _____

7+2 = _____

5+2 = _____

6+4 = _____

2+6 = _____

3+5 = _____

3+2 = _____

Number of Problems: 12   Number Correct: _____   Time to complete: ____ min.

Name: _____

Skill:

Float the Boats

Fill the blank with the correct numeral to keep your boat afloat.

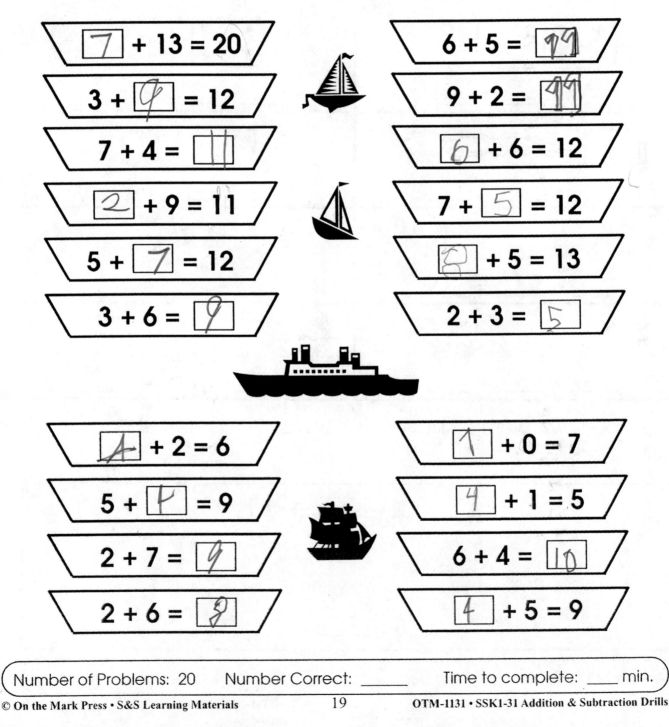

$\boxed{7} + 13 = 20$	$6 + 5 = \boxed{11}$
$3 + \boxed{9} = 12$	$9 + 2 = \boxed{11}$
$7 + 4 = \boxed{11}$	$\boxed{6} + 6 = 12$
$\boxed{2} + 9 = 11$	$7 + \boxed{5} = 12$
$5 + \boxed{7} = 12$	$\boxed{8} + 5 = 13$
$3 + 6 = \boxed{9}$	$2 + 3 = \boxed{5}$

$\boxed{4} + 2 = 6$	$\boxed{7} + 0 = 7$
$5 + \boxed{4} = 9$	$\boxed{4} + 1 = 5$
$2 + 7 = \boxed{9}$	$6 + 4 = \boxed{10}$
$2 + 6 = \boxed{8}$	$\boxed{4} + 5 = 9$

Number of Problems: 20   Number Correct: _____   Time to complete: ____ min.

Name: _____

Skill:

Addition Sentences

Write a number story that matches each picture.

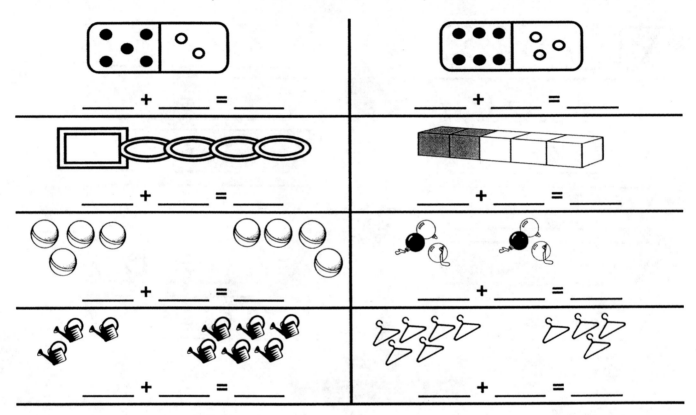

___ + ___ = ___

___ + ___ = ___

___ + ___ = ___

___ + ___ = ___

___ + ___ = ___

___ + ___ = ___

___ + ___ = ___

___ + ___ = ___

Draw your own picture. Have someone write a number story for your picture.

_____ + _____ = _____

Number of Problems: 8   Number Correct: _____   Time to complete: ____ min.

Skill: _____

Column Addition

1. $\begin{array}{r} 1 \\ 1 \\ +2 \\ \hline \end{array}$	2. $\begin{array}{r} 2 \\ 1 \\ +3 \\ \hline \end{array}$	3. $\begin{array}{r} 3 \\ 1 \\ +1 \\ \hline \end{array}$	4. $\begin{array}{r} 4 \\ 1 \\ +2 \\ \hline \end{array}$	1. $\begin{array}{r} 1 \\ 2 \\ +3 \\ \hline \end{array}$
5. $\begin{array}{r} 5 \\ 2 \\ +1 \\ \hline \end{array}$	6. $\begin{array}{r} 6 \\ 1 \\ +3 \\ \hline \end{array}$	7. $\begin{array}{r} 7 \\ 2 \\ +1 \\ \hline \end{array}$	8. $\begin{array}{r} 8 \\ 3 \\ +2 \\ \hline \end{array}$	4. $\begin{array}{r} 4 \\ 6 \\ +5 \\ \hline \end{array}$
9. $\begin{array}{r} 9 \\ 1 \\ +0 \\ \hline \end{array}$	1. $\begin{array}{r} 1 \\ 2 \\ +2 \\ \hline \end{array}$	2. $\begin{array}{r} 2 \\ 2 \\ +4 \\ \hline \end{array}$	3. $\begin{array}{r} 3 \\ 2 \\ +3 \\ \hline \end{array}$	8. $\begin{array}{r} 8 \\ 9 \\ +7 \\ \hline \end{array}$
4. $\begin{array}{r} 4 \\ 2 \\ +3 \\ \hline \end{array}$	5. $\begin{array}{r} 5 \\ 4 \\ +0 \\ \hline \end{array}$	6. $\begin{array}{r} 6 \\ 2 \\ +4 \\ \hline \end{array}$	7. $\begin{array}{r} 7 \\ 3 \\ +2 \\ \hline \end{array}$	8. $\begin{array}{r} 8 \\ 1 \\ +4 \\ \hline \end{array}$
5. $\begin{array}{r} 5 \\ 2 \\ +4 \\ \hline \end{array}$	5. $\begin{array}{r} 5 \\ 6 \\ +1 \\ \hline \end{array}$	9. $\begin{array}{r} 9 \\ 2 \\ +3 \\ \hline \end{array}$	8. $\begin{array}{r} 8 \\ 3 \\ +5 \\ \hline \end{array}$	7. $\begin{array}{r} 7 \\ 6 \\ +3 \\ \hline \end{array}$

Number of Problems: 25   Number Correct: _____   Time to complete: ____ min.

Name: _____

Skill:
Two Digit Addition
No Regrouping

10 + 12	11 + 16	12 + 17	13 + 15
11 + 14	14 + 15	16 + 11	15 + 10
12 + 13	17 + 12	18 + 11	19 + 10
13 + 10	12 + 11	13 + 14	10 + 15
14 + 12	18 + 10	12 + 16	13 + 16

Number of Problems: 20   Number Correct: _____   Time to complete: ____ min.

Skill:
Two Digit Addition
No Regrouping

```
  12        11        10        43
+ 16      + 15      + 27      + 15
```

```
  17        21        13        42
+ 11      + 14      + 25      + 17
```

```
  14        13        32        26
+ 14      + 12      + 17      + 12
```

```
  23        53        47        63
+ 15      + 16      + 21      + 25
```

```
  30        25        36        55
+ 29      + 14      + 23      + 22
```

Number of Problems: 20   Number Correct: _____   Time to complete: ____ min.

Skill:
Two Digit Addition
With Regrouping

13 + 7	18 + 4	11 + 9	17 + 4	14 + 6
15 + 6	15 + 8	16 + 7	19 + 6	19 + 9
16 + 7	17 + 8	13 + 9	16 + 9	17 + 5
13 + 8	17 + 7	18 + 6	15 + 7	17 + 3
19 + 5	12 + 8	19 + 1	17 + 6	16 + 4
17 + 9	19 + 8	16 + 5	12 + 9	18 + 7

Number of Problems: 30   Number Correct: _____   Time to complete: ____ min.

Two Digit Addition

Skill:

With Regrouping   No Regrouping

70	40	64	21	57
42	+ 26	+ 46	+ 16	+ 32
12	6		31	89

59	84	59	52	55
26	+ 38	+ 3	+ 24	+ 42
			16	97

50	80	96	15	62
45	+ 69	+ 52	+ 13	+ 2
			28	64

96	92	49	56	68
62	+ 35	+ 49	+ 40	+ 47
			96	115

98	73	28	72	+ 74
17	+ 16	+ 26	+ 45	+ 50
			117	124

44	84	81	61	64
19	+ 80	+ 61	+ 56	+ 42
			117	106

Number of Problems: 30   Number Correct: _____   Time to complete: ____ min.

Skill: _____

Word Problems

Sarah's brother blew up 9 ◯ for her party. Her father blew up 18 ◯. How many balloons are there all together?

_____ + _____ = _____

A farmer has 12 🐄 in a field. 13 🐄 are in the barn. How many 🐄 does the farmer have all together?

_____ + _____ = _____

The girls in Miss Brown's class are collecting ✎ to donate to the hospital nursery. Keisha's group have collected 13 ✎, Emma's group have collected 12 ✎, and Cory's group have ✎✎✎✎✎. How many ✎ are there all together?

_____ + _____ + _____ = _____

The farmer's wife collects the ◯ every morning. The first hen layed 5 ◯. The second hen layed 6 ◯. The last hen layed 2 ◯. How many ◯ were there all together?

_____ + _____ + _____ = _____

Emma and Madison went to the library to get information about lizards. Emma borrowed 3 📖 on lizards. Madison borrowed 4 📖 on lizards. How many 📖 are there all together?

_____ + _____ = _____

Jordan and Keith went to the beach. Jordon built 4 🏰. Keith built 3 🏰. How many 🏰 did the boys build all together?

_____ + _____ = _____

Number of Problems: 6   Number Correct: _____   Time to complete: ____ min.

Skill:

Two Digit Addition

With Regrouping   No Regrouping

| 26 | 42 | 65 | 78 |
| + 65 | + 43 | + 34 | + 93 |

| 49 | 15 | 35 | 85 |
| + 62 | + 11 | + 44 | + 29 |

| 41 | 53 | 12 | 53 |
| + 40 | + 46 | + 17 | + 26 |

| 17 | 33 | 57 | 78 |
| + 55 | + 97 | + 62 | + 56 |

| 25 | 73 | 63 | 47 |
| + 38 | + 33 | + 15 | + 88 |

| 12 | 56 | 12 | 24 |
| + 85 | + 10 | + 63 | + 65 |

Number of Problems: 20   Number Correct: _____   Time to complete: _____ min.

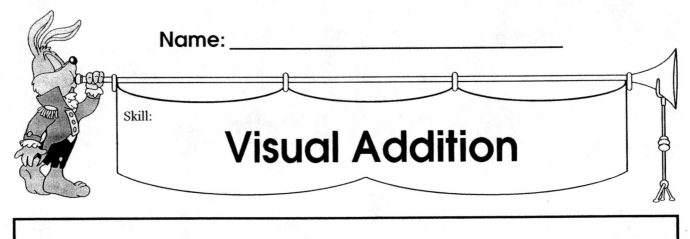

Name: _____

Skill:

Visual Addition

How many geese are there?

_____

How many leaves are falling?

_____

How many boys are there?

_____

Add these all together. _____

How many penguins are there? _____

How many panda bears can you see? _____

How many polar bears can you see? _____

Add these all together. _____

Number of Problems: 2   Number Correct: _____   Time to complete: ____ min.

Skill:

Two Digit Addition

With Regrouping   No Regrouping

68 + 22	26 + 25	35 + 52	49 + 43
63 + 26	26 + 23	34 + 48	32 + 28
11 + 18	59 + 11	27 + 71	90 + 9
88 + 8	49 + 29	5 + 71	38 + 45
80 + 10	63 + 24	68 + 5	27 + 44
73 + 14	22 + 57	39 + 50	48 + 47

Number of Problems: 24   Number Correct: _____   Time to complete: ____ min.

Name: _____

Picture Puzzles

There were 🍄🍄🍄🍄🍄 in the back yard. It rained all morning. After the rain, six more 🍄 had grown. How many 🍄 are in the back yard?

_____ + _____ = _____

A 👧 bought 👗 👗 . She also bought 🧤 and a 👒 . How many items did she buy all together?

_____ + _____ + _____ = _____

Seven 🐭 are eating a large piece of 🧀 . 🐭🐭🐭🐭 join them. How many 🐭 are there eating the 🧀 ?

_____ + _____ = _____

For his birthday, Jordan got an 🐟 with seven 🐟 . He bought six more 🐟 . How many fish did he have all together?

_____ + _____ = _____

Number of Problems: 4   Number Correct: _____   Time to complete: ____ min.

Name: _____

Skill:

More Rocket Ship Math

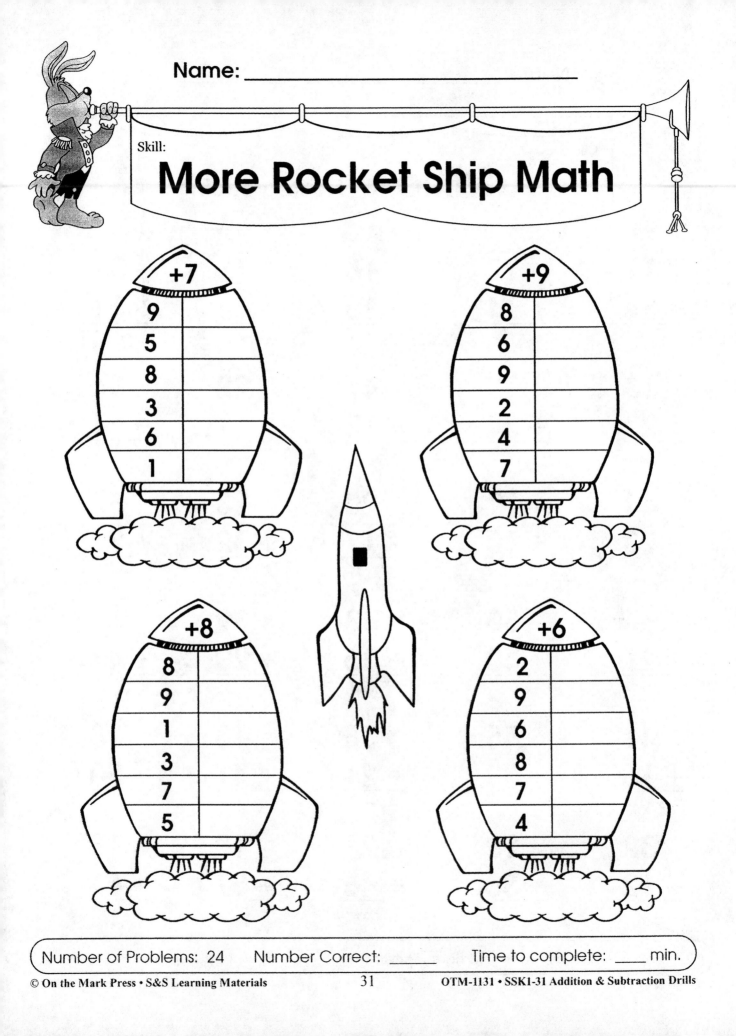

+7

9	
5	
8	
3	
6	
1	

+9

8	
6	
9	
2	
4	
7	

+8

8	
9	
1	
3	
7	
5	

+6

2	
9	
6	
8	
7	
4	

Number of Problems: 24   Number Correct: _____   Time to complete: ____ min.

Addition - No Regrouping

Skill:

11 + 34	12 + 14	18 + 10	15 + 12	38 + 11
13 + 23	10 + 24	47 + 12	22 + 11	34 + 24
44 + 23	17 + 10	20 + 17	23 + 32	32 + 25
54 + 21	50 + 40	43 + 36	39 + 20	12 + 44
41 + 16	45 + 32	38 + 21	13 + 41	18 + 50
32 + 12	19 + 30	21 + 46	12 + 57	18 + 61

Number of Problems: 30   Number Correct: _____   Time to complete: ____ min.

Name: _____

Addition Wheels

Add the number in the middle to each number in turn. Then write your answer in the blank. Two have been done for you.

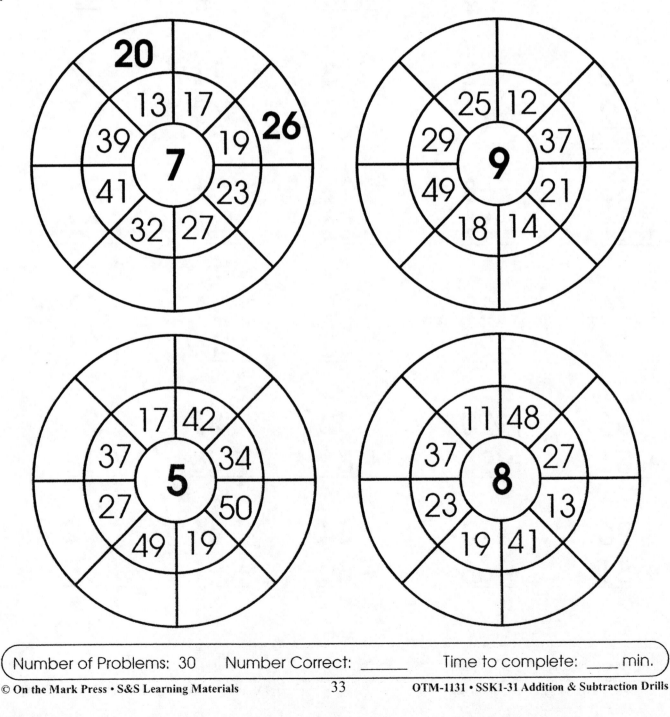

Number of Problems: 30   Number Correct: _____   Time to complete: ____ min.

Skill:

Addition

With Regrouping   No Regrouping

14	16	6	2	4
+ 15	+ 5	+ 13	+ 4	+ 7

0	2	3	11	17
+ 9	+ 11	+ 7	+ 0	+ 3

33	68	26	91	74
+ 11	+ 19	+ 22	+ 14	+ 24

76	52	5	11	31
+ 19	+ 25	+ 3	+ 14	+ 21

56	20	32	81	21
+ 51	+ 96	+ 81	+ 28	+ 14

96	13	64	86	42
+ 51	+ 63	+ 30	+ 91	+ 89

Number of Problems: 30   Number Correct: _____   Time to complete: ____ min.

Skill: ____

Bubble Addition

313 + 37 = ____

____ + 127 = 439

577 + ____ = 640

747 + 258 = 1005

420 + 88 = 508

189 + 127 = 316

971 + 181 = 1152

399 + 129 = ____

____ + 74 = 398

211 + 122 = ____

43 + 75 = ____

13 + 27 = ____

427 + 201 = ____

98 + 47 = ____

Number of Problems: 14   Number Correct: _____   Time to complete: ____ min.

© On the Mark Press • S&S Learning Materials   35   OTM-1131 • SSK1-31 Addition & Subtraction Drills

Skill:

Three Digit Addition

With Regrouping   No Regrouping

299 + 237	263 + 126	323 + 167	832 + 3	443 + 353
379 + 67	119 + 109	214 + 128	338 + 210	328 + 48
208 + 110	141 + 130	159 + 140	727 + 212	528 + 100
166 + 166	665 + 156	820 + 719	966 + 93	459 + 274
856 + 563	218 + 76	820 + 519	406 + 66	315 + 269
559 + 473	817 + 125	649 + 506	774 + 360	528 + 179

Number of Problems: 30   Number Correct: _____   Time to complete: ____ min.

Skill:
Two Digit Column Addition

59	52	55	80	96
21	21	42	69	52
3	+ 7	+ 9	+ 11	+ 3

9	15	37	48	15
2	11	24	20	13
7	+ 10	+ 10	+ 12	+ 9

94	62	92	56	68
14	31	35	40	47
27	+ 2	+ 11	+ 9	+ 9

20	63	22	90	42
18	61	12	70	24
5	+ 36	+ 2	+ 10	+ 7

70	65	73	40	73
38	23	37	23	56
56	+ 3	+ 13	+ 17	+ 18

39	63	77	39	25
26	49	48	24	18
+ 7	+ 20	+ 23	+ 12	+ 13

Number of Problems: 30   Number Correct: _____   Time to complete: ____ min.

Three Digit Column Addition

Skill:

173	437	872	225
157	318	526	191
93	+ 109	+ 93	+ 74

139	998	123	297
83	793	101	134
17	+ 27	+ 97	+ 121

171	164	171	896
151	149	139	539
142	+ 70	+ 101	+ 40

191	198	250	207
158	99	116	206
97	+ 78	+ 108	+ 105

874	441	132	754
298	123	109	330
33	+ 100	+ 89	+ 199

Number of Problems: 20   Number Correct: _____   Time to complete: ____ min.

Name: _____

Skill: _____

Balloon Addition

643
+ 503

995
+ 225

171
+ 139

703
+ 496

488
+ 484

998
+ 793

184
+ 40

307
+ 290

Number of Problems: 8   Number Correct: _____   Time to complete: ____ min.

© On the Mark Press • S&S Learning Materials   39   OTM-1131 • SSK1-31 Addition & Subtraction Drills

What's Missing?

```
   3 □        2 4        □ 7        2 □
 + □ 2      + □ □      + 5 □      + □ 4
 ─────      ─────      ─────      ─────
   5 1        6 6        6 9        4 0


   5 2        □ 0        3 □        □ □
 + □ □      + 1 □      + □ 4      + 3 7
 ─────      ─────      ─────      ─────
   7 3        6 0        5 2       1 2 4


   8 □        2 □        4 □        □ 6
 + □ 8      +   □      + □ 6      + □ 0
 ─────      ─────      ─────      ─────
  1 3 1       3 1        8 4        2 6


   2 □        8 6         □         □ 7
 +   □      + □ □      +   6      + 5 □
 ─────      ─────      ─────      ─────
   3 7       1 2 1       1 5        6 7


   5 1        □ □        □ 8        7 □
 + 2 8      + 2 6      + 1 □      + □ 5
 ─────      ─────      ─────      ─────
   □ □        5 4        3 4       1 1 7
```

Number of Problems: 20   Number Correct: _____   Time to complete: ____ min.

© On the Mark Press • S&S Learning Materials   40   OTM-1131 • SSK1-31 Addition & Subtraction Drills

Name: _____

Skill:

You're a Star!

Solve these problems. When you are finished, color the stars blue if the sums are greater than 50, and yellow for less than 50.

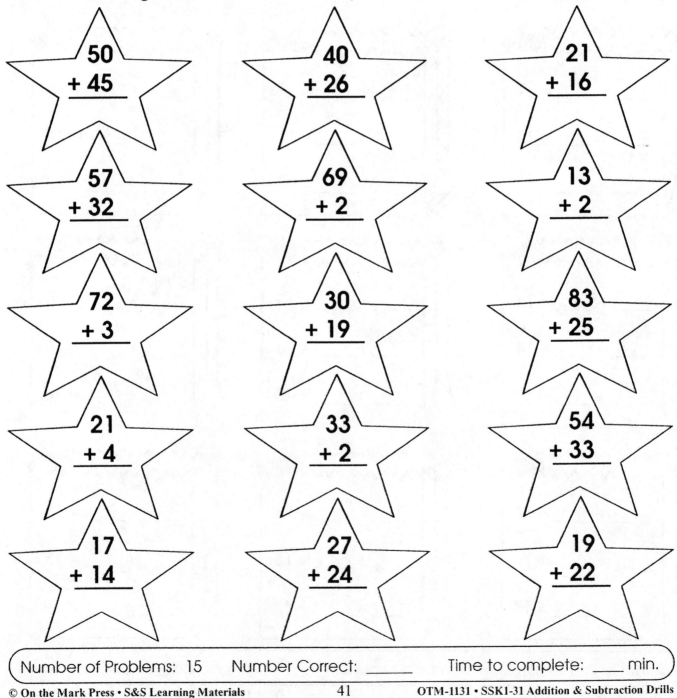

$$50 + 45$$

$$40 + 26$$

$$21 + 16$$

$$57 + 32$$

$$69 + 2$$

$$13 + 2$$

$$72 + 3$$

$$30 + 19$$

$$83 + 25$$

$$21 + 4$$

$$33 + 2$$

$$54 + 33$$

$$17 + 14$$

$$27 + 24$$

$$19 + 22$$

Number of Problems: 15   Number Correct: _____   Time to complete: ____ min.

Skill:

Grocery Bag Addition

Write three different number sentences that will give you the correct answer.

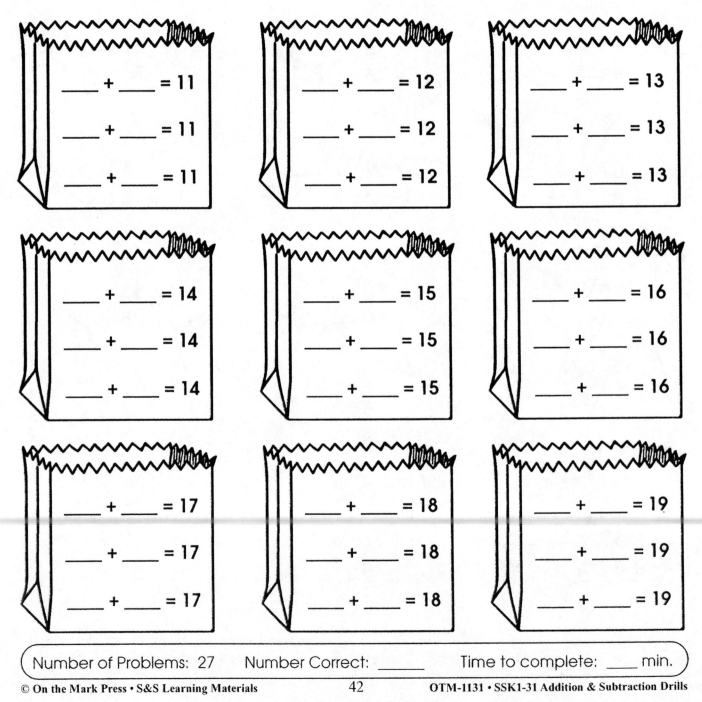

___ + ___ = 11
___ + ___ = 11
___ + ___ = 11

___ + ___ = 12
___ + ___ = 12
___ + ___ = 12

___ + ___ = 13
___ + ___ = 13
___ + ___ = 13

___ + ___ = 14
___ + ___ = 14
___ + ___ = 14

___ + ___ = 15
___ + ___ = 15
___ + ___ = 15

___ + ___ = 16
___ + ___ = 16
___ + ___ = 16

___ + ___ = 17
___ + ___ = 17
___ + ___ = 17

___ + ___ = 18
___ + ___ = 18
___ + ___ = 18

___ + ___ = 19
___ + ___ = 19
___ + ___ = 19

Number of Problems: 27   Number Correct: _____   Time to complete: ____ min.

Skill: _____

Word Problems

On Tuesday, Miss Jones took her class to the library. The girls borrowed 23 books. The boys borrowed 8 books. How many books were borrowed all together?

_____ + _____ = _____

Mrs. Robinson is our mail person. In September, she delivered 43 letters to our house, 29 in October, and 74 in December. How many letters did she deliver all together?

_____ + _____ + _____ = _____

A board game has 23 blue coins, 7 red coins, and 12 yellow coins. How many are there all together?

_____ + _____ + _____ = _____

There are 27 horses in the farmer's field. The farmer has 29 horses still in the barn. How many horses does the farmer have all together?

_____ + _____ = _____

Number of Problems: 4   Number Correct: _____   Time to complete: ____ min.

Skill:

Addition - No Regrouping

30 + 29	65 + 20	21 + 13	65 + 12
15 + 14	17 + 42	14 + 13	26 + 42
22 + 13	65 + 32	22 + 17	37 + 51
31 + 12	76 + 12	56 + 23	44 + 33
21 + 30	82 + 17	67 + 11	25 + 20
33 + 25	74 + 15	53 + 16	46 + 12

Number of Problems: 24   Number Correct: _____   Time to complete: ____ min.

Skill:

Addition - No Regrouping

13 + 42	44 + 13	62 + 17	50 + 20
17 + 30	24 + 15	30 + 19	83 + 14
53 + 25	17 + 31	46 + 10	32 + 16
74 + 12	23 + 43	73 + 12	63 + 15
45 + 21	16 + 12	51 + 48	67 + 11
15 + 60	24 + 53	72 + 16	80 + 19

Number of Problems: 24   Number Correct: _____   Time to complete: ____ min.

Skill:

Column Addition
No Regrouping

250	46	501	58
133	20	114	10
+ 401	+ 13	+ 204	+ 21

416	60	323	48
102	15	132	11
+ 401	+ 24	+ 121	+ 10

22	270	340	34
13	104	125	22
+ 41	+ 115	+ 311	+ 10

301	13	22	203
242	15	26	241
+ 155	+ 11	+ 40	+ 335

Number of Problems: 16   Number Correct: _____   Time to complete: ____ min.

Skill:

Adding Decimals

3.69 + 2.41	2.51 + 3.27	4.29 + 0.83	3.48 + 9.48
6.34 + 2.78	4.99 + 2.73	8.34 + 2.69	1.21 + 2.48
4.77 + 2.88	1.19 + 9.47	4.49 + 2.02	8.01 + 0.98
7.47 + 3.69	9.88 + 4.66	6.53 + 3.07	2.47 + 0.98
3.05 + 1.81	2.25 + 1.89	8.79 + 3.36	4.20 + 3.63
4.84 + 0.57	8.04 + 3.01	9.92 + 16	2.30 + 1.42

Number of Problems: 24   Number Correct: _____   Time to complete: ____ min.

Three Digit Addition

Skill:

No Regrouping

507 + 100	761 + 137	242 + 143	852 + 146
637 + 230	110 + 339	538 + 311	431 + 141
410 + 186	620 + 149	800 + 169	765 + 220
454 + 104	606 + 362	223 + 120	406 + 271
459 + 100	390 + 108	542 + 216	400 + 271
620 + 149	732 + 201	519 + 440	443 + 124

Number of Problems: 24   Number Correct: _____   Time to complete: _____ min.

Skill:

Column Addition - Three Digits

With Regrouping   No Regrouping

112	167	314	618
401	114	195	262
+ 364	+ 192	+ 107	+ 174

101	768	648	655
423	245	459	390
+ 434	+ 109	+ 292	+ 137

212	838	345	524
403	783	117	417
+ 364	+ 550	+ 92	+ 393

383	618	354	829
147	465	106	214
+ 138	+ 377	+ 97	+ 177

758	944	434	851
745	779	459	893
+ 770	+ 386	+ 478	+ 879

Number of Problems: 20   Number Correct: _____   Time to complete: _____ min.

Two Digit Addition
Skill:
With Regrouping

23 + 18	56 + 24	47 + 38	29 + 26
44 + 28	19 + 12	49 + 9	67 + 18
92 + 88	66 + 48	86 + 48	49 + 12
76 + 49	85 + 55	89 + 12	85 + 67
36 + 15	69 + 57	97 + 84	78 + 73
33 + 28	16 + 14	89 + 35	96 + 96

Number of Problems: 24   Number Correct: _____   Time to complete: ____ min.

Three Digit Addition

Skill:

With Regrouping

396 + 177	229 + 109	283 + 208	527 + 392
942 + 528	704 + 367	568 + 17	894 + 638
389 + 247	386 + 277	859 + 235	669 + 539
274 + 118	380 + 157	819 + 533	178 + 157
655 + 237	515 + 505	489 + 165	760 + 556
857 + 175	568 + 355	596 + 288	891 + 798

Number of Problems: 24   Number Correct: _____   Time to complete: ____ min.

Skill:

Four Digit Addition
No Regrouping

3204 + 1033	4153 + 4023	2957 + 1042	4862 + 4113
3904 + 2085	5264 + 1523	7290 + 2609	1049 + 4950
6724 + 2133	3364 + 2404	8814 + 1164	5320 + 2349
9319 + 1640	1541 + 4338	2324 + 2145	3764 + 4023
5839 + 3120	7575 + 2222	6917 + 2040	7823 + 2033
9241 + 444	6628 + 2241	9041 + 956	8450 + 1528

Number of Problems: 24   Number Correct: _____   Time to complete: ____ min.

Four Digit Addition

Skill:

With Regrouping

1629	9351	4671	2955
1456	+ 7595	+ 2191	+ 715

1338	8495	7989	9965
1142	+ 2143	+ 2181	+ 4209

4849	8651	5683	3894
3912	+ 2817	+ 1441	+ 2323

8530	5845	6299	8186
6928	+ 3924	+ 4808	+ 915

7803	5926	8450	7823
6982	+ 2929	+ 3838	+ 2937

8076	3799	3798	7988
3387	+ 3107	+ 1157	+ 3849

Number of Problems: 24   Number Correct: _____   Time to complete: ____ min.

Skill:

Word Problems

Emma and her friend needed to get new baseball gear. They each bought a new ball glove that cost $4.50 each. They bought one baseball to share. The ball cost $1.25. Then they found socks for $2.25 a pair and bought one pair each. How much did they spend all together?

_____

Jordan has 7 toy cars, 3 toy trucks and 1 toy boat. Liam has 11 toy cars, 5 toy trucks and 1 toy motorcycle. How many toys are there all together?

_____

Brittany and Keisha wanted to go to the movie. Admission was $3.50 each. Popcorn and a drink cost $2.50. How much money would they need to go to the movie?

_____

On Monday, 623 people rode the subway. On Tuesday, there were 891. How many people rode the subway all together?

_____

Madison invited 6 girls and 3 boys to her birthday party. How many children were invited to the party?

_____

Number of Problems: 5   Number Correct: _____   Time to complete: ____ min.

Skill: _____

Mixed Addition

37 24	241 + 149	58 + 11	632 + 359	72 + 29
374 218	26 + 32	258 + 224	43 + 25	423 + 176
41 19	468 + 232	39 + 27	721 + 235	74 + 23
501 268	82 + 63	349 + 275	587 + 293	19 + 26
62 27	623 + 347	89 + 76	52 + 39	47 + 68
17 + 17	999 + 321	22 + 39	888 + 112	23 + 17

Number of Problems: 30   Number Correct: _____   Time to complete: ____ min.

Skill: _____

Addition Wheels

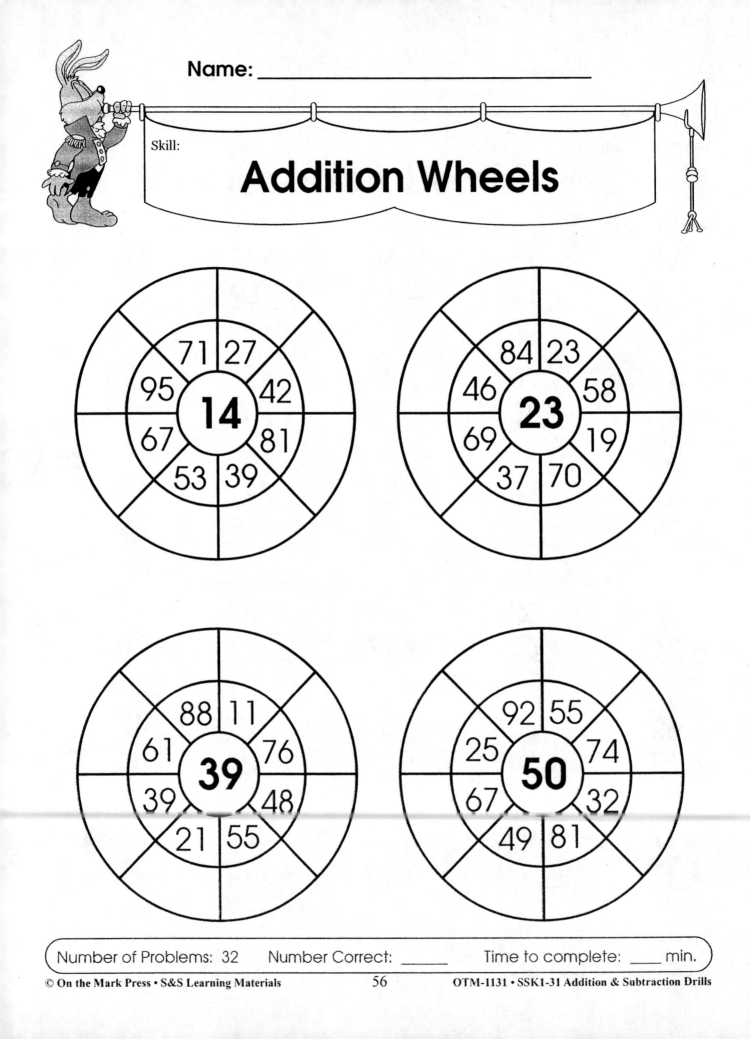

Number of Problems: 32   Number Correct: _____   Time to complete: ____ min.

© On the Mark Press • S&S Learning Materials   56   OTM-1131 • SSK1-31 Addition & Subtraction Drills

Name: _____

Skill: Adding Decimals

With Regrouping   No Regrouping

6.98 + 6.08	9.94 + 9.43	1.77 + 1.21	2.34 + 1.33
3.68 + 1.81	1.52 + 1.30	6.26 + 1.35	6.33 + 2.13
7.75 + 1.03	5.50 + 1.31	1.61 + 2.34	8.29 + 2.14
7.17 + 1.13	2.10 + 2.64	2.32 + 1.36	5.35 + 2.00
9.24 + 4.34	7.23 + 2.56	6.83 + 6.35	3.55 + 2.33

Number of Problems: 20   Number Correct: _____   Time to complete: ____ min.

Skill: _____

Word Problems

Jordy's grade 4 class is having a barbecue to raise money. They are selling hot dogs and hamburgers. There are 120 hot dogs and 85 hamburgers. How many are there all together?

_____

A bee keeper has 25 000 bees. In one month, he collected 41 gallons (155 liters), 37 gallons (140 liters), 29 gallons (110 liters), and 23 gallons (87 liters) of honey. How much honey did he gather all together?

_____

Emma's kite is flying 280 feet (85 meters) high. She tied on another 185 feet (56 meters) of kite string. Now how high will her kite fly?

_____

The astronomy club counted the number of satellites they saw while star gazing. On Friday, they saw 17 satellites. On Saturday, they saw 24. How many did they see all together?

_____

Number of Problems: 4   Number Correct: _____   Time to complete: ____ min.

Skill: _____

Review

With Regrouping   **No Regrouping**

43 + 27	15 + 12	66 + 17	84 + 16	22 + 19
72 + 39	52 + 17	82 + 13	29 + 24	75 + 14
193 + 177	282 + 106	379 + 120	546 + 242	399 + 100
127 + 112	168 + 111	298 + 201	652 + 333	802 + 198
17 + 11	127 + 122	88 + 12	369 + 221	773 + 884
34 + 26	83 + 15	6 + 4	78 + 29	694 + 281

Number of Problems: 30   Number Correct: _____   Time to complete: ____ min.

Skill:

The Sky's the Limit

Do the problem, then color the kites. If the answer is greater than 50, color the kite blue; less than 50, color it green.

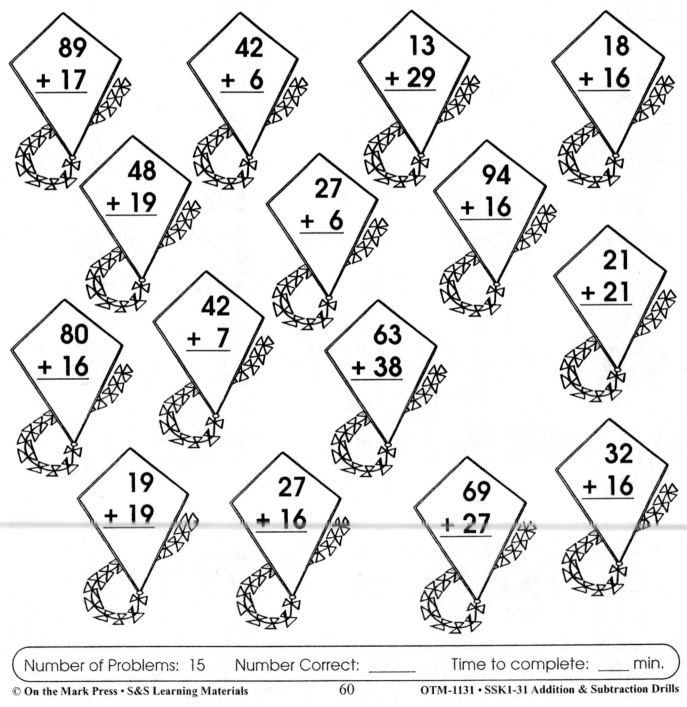

89
+ 17

42
+ 6

13
+ 29

18
+ 16

48
+ 19

27
+ 6

94
+ 16

80
+ 16

42
+ 7

63
+ 38

21
+ 21

19
+ 19

27
+ 16

69
+ 27

32
+ 16

Number of Problems: 15   Number Correct: _____   Time to complete: ____ min.

Name: _____

Four Digit Addition

With Regrouping   No Regrouping

1629	9351	4671	2955
+ 1456	+ 7595	+ 2191	+ 715

1338	8495	7989	9965
+ 1142	+ 2143	+ 2181	+ 4209

4849	8651	5683	3894
+ 3912	+ 2817	+ 1441	+ 2323

8530	5845	6299	8186
+ 6928	+ 3924	+ 4808	+ 915

7803	5926	8450	7823
+ 6982	+ 2929	+ 3838	+ 2937

Number of Problems: 20   Number Correct: _____   Time to complete: ____ min.

Subtraction Drill Work Sheets

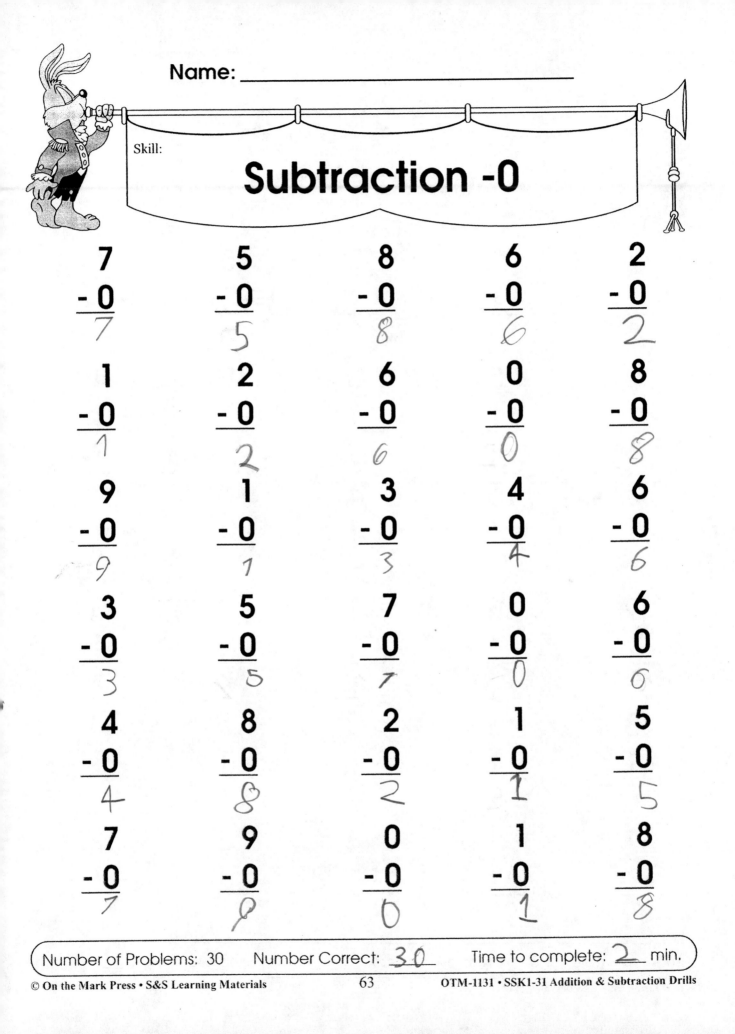

Name: _____

Skill:

Subtraction -0

7 - 0 *7*	5 - 0 *5*	8 - 0 *8*	6 - 0 *6*	2 - 0 *2*
1 - 0 *1*	2 - 0 *2*	6 - 0 *6*	0 - 0 *0*	8 - 0 *8*
9 - 0 *9*	1 - 0 *1*	3 - 0 *3*	4 - 0 *4*	6 - 0 *6*
3 - 0 *3*	5 - 0 *5*	7 - 0 *7*	0 - 0 *0*	6 - 0 *6*
4 - 0 *4*	8 - 0 *8*	2 - 0 *2*	1 - 0 *1*	5 - 0 *5*
7 - 0 *7*	9 - 0 *9*	0 - 0 *0*	1 - 0 *1*	8 - 0 *8*

Number of Problems: 30   Number Correct: _30_   Time to complete: _2_ min.

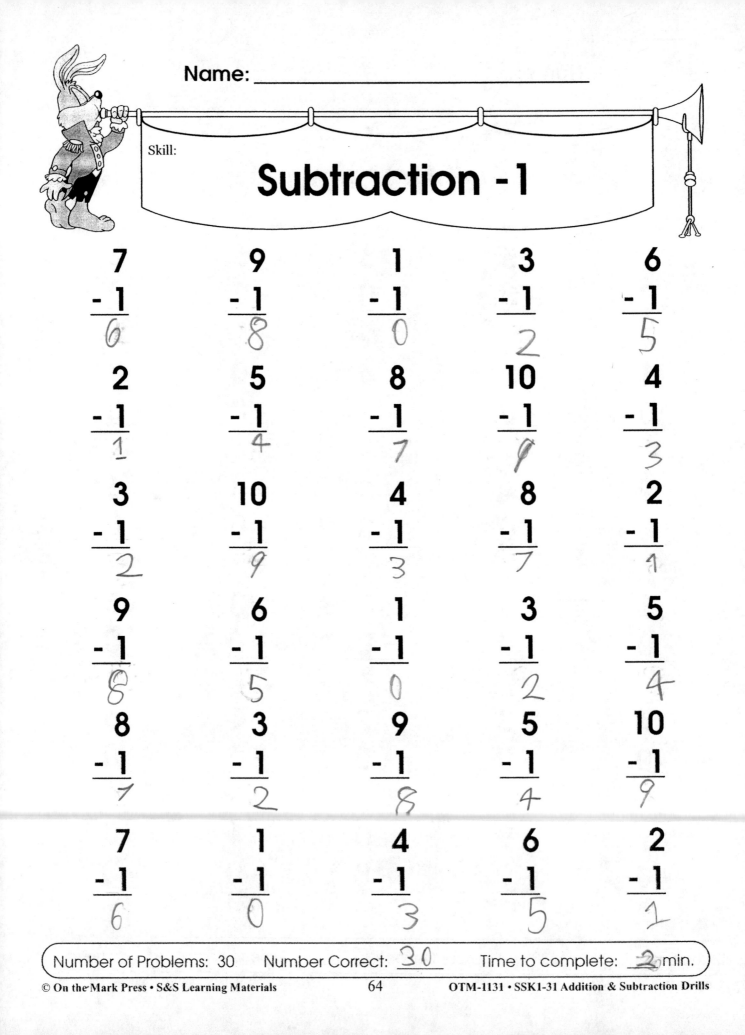

Name: _____

Skill:

Subtraction -1

7 - 1 6	9 - 1 8	1 - 1 0	3 - 1 2	6 - 1 5
2 - 1 1	5 - 1 4	8 - 1 7	10 - 1 9	4 - 1 3
3 - 1 2	10 - 1 9	4 - 1 3	8 - 1 7	2 - 1 1
9 - 1 8	6 - 1 5	1 - 1 0	3 - 1 2	5 - 1 4
8 - 1 7	3 - 1 2	9 - 1 8	5 - 1 4	10 - 1 9
7 - 1 6	1 - 1 0	4 - 1 3	6 - 1 5	2 - 1 1

Number of Problems: 30   Number Correct: 30   Time to complete: 2 min.

    OTM-1131 • SSK1-31 Addition & Subtraction Drills

Skill:

Subtraction -2

2	4	9	5	3
- 2	- 2	- 2	- 2	- 2
0	*2*	*7*	*3*	*1*

6	8	10	7	2
- 2	- 2	- 2	- 2	- 2
4	*6*	*8*	*5*	*0*

8	4	10	9	5
- 2	- 2	- 2	- 2	- 2
6	*2*	*8*	*7*	*3*

10	6	3	7	2
- 2	- 2	- 2	- 2	- 2
8	*4*	*1*	*5*	*0*

9	2	6	4	8
- 2	- 2	- 2	- 2	- 2
7	*0*	*4*	*2*	*6*

7	5	3	10	9
- 2	- 2	- 2	- 2	- 2
5	*3*	*1*	*8*	*7*

Number of Problems: 30   Number Correct: **30**   Time to complete: **5** min.

Name: _____

Subtraction -3

7	10	6	4	5
- 3	- 3	- 3	- 3	- 3
4	*7*	*3*	*1*	*2*

4	8	7	10	9
- 3	- 3	- 3	- 3	- 3
1	*5*	*4*	*7*	*6*

6	3	5	7	10
- 3	- 3	- 3	- 3	- 3
3	*0*	*2*	*4*	*7*

8	9	4	5	3
- 3	- 3	- 3	- 3	- 3
5	*6*	*1*	*2*	*0*

6	8	10	7	9
- 3	- 3	- 3	- 3	- 3
3	*5*	*7*	*4*	*6*

5	3	7	6	4
- 3	- 3	- 3	- 3	- 3
2	*0*	*4*	*3*	*1*

Number of Problems: 30   Number Correct: *30*   Time to complete: *5* min.

Skill:

Subtraction -4

10	7	4	9	5
$-\,4$	$-\,4$	$-\,4$	$-\,4$	$-\,4$
6	*3*	*0*	*5*	*1*

8	10	6	8	7
$-\,4$	$-\,4$	$-\,4$	$-\,4$	$-\,4$
4	*6*	*2*	*4*	*3*

9	4	10	8	5
$-\,4$	$-\,4$	$-\,4$	$-\,4$	$-\,4$
5	*0*	*6*	*4*	*1*

7	4	9	6	5
$-\,4$	$-\,4$	$-\,4$	$-\,4$	$-\,4$
3	*0*	*5*	*2*	*1*

4	8	6	9	7
$-\,4$	$-\,4$	$-\,4$	$-\,4$	$-\,4$
0	*4*	*2*	*5*	*3*

10	8	6	4	5
$-\,4$	$-\,4$	$-\,4$	$-\,4$	$-\,4$
6	*4*	*2*	*0*	*1*

Number of Problems: 30   Number Correct: __*30*__   Time to complete: __*2*__ min.

Skill:

Subtraction -5

9	12	7	10	5
- 5	- 5	- 5	- 5	- 5
4	7	2	5	0

11	6	8	12	7
- 5	- 5	- 5	- 5	- 5
6	1	3	7	2

5	9	10	6	11
- 5	- 5	- 5	- 5	- 5
0	4	5	1	6

12	6	7	8	10
- 5	- 5	- 5	- 5	- 5
7	1	2	3	5

11	9	10	7	5
- 5	- 5	- 5	- 5	- 5
8	4	5	2	0

8	11	5	8	9
- 5	- 5	- 5	- 5	- 5
3	6	0	3	4

Number of Problems: 30   Number Correct: _____   Time to complete: ___ min.

Skill:

Subtraction -6

13 - 6 *7*	9 - 6 *3*	6 - 6 *0*	7 - 6 *1*	11 - 6 *5*
8 - 6 *2*	12 - 6 *6*	7 - 6 *1*	10 - 6 *4*	12 - 6 *6*
8 - 6 *2*	11 - 6 *5*	10 - 6 *4*	13 - 6 *7*	9 - 6 *3*
6 - 6 *0*	9 - 6 *3*	13 - 6 *7*	10 - 6 *4*	7 - 6 *1*
11 - 6 *5*	8 - 6 *2*	9 - 6 *3*	11 - 6 *5*	12 - 6 *6*
13 - 6 *7*	6 - 6 *0*	8 - 6 *2*	12 - 6 *6*	9 - 6 *3*

Number of Problems: 30   Number Correct: _____   Time to complete: ____ min.

Skill:

Subtraction -7

11 - 7 *4*	9 - 7 *2*	15 - 7 *8*	12 - 7 *5*	14 - 7 *7*
10 - 7 *3*	13 - 7 *5*	8 - 7 *1*	9 - 7 *2*	16 - 7 *9*
15 - 7 *8*	16 - 7 *9*	12 - 7 *5*	9 - 7 *2*	7 - 7 *0*
11 - 7 *4*	14 - 7 *7*	8 - 7 *1*	13 - 7 *5*	10 - 7 *3*
9 - 7 *2*	16 - 7 *9*	7 - 7 *0*	12 - 7 *5*	15 - 7 *8*
11 - 7 *4*	14 - 7 *7*	8 - 7 *1*	13 - 7 *5*	9 - 7 *2*

Number of Problems: 30   Number Correct: _____   Time to complete: ____ min.

Skill:

Subtraction -8

15 − 8	13 − 8	17 − 8	11 − 8	9 − 8
8 − 8	12 − 8	10 − 8	16 − 8	14 − 8
10 − 8	13 − 8	9 − 8	8 − 8	17 − 8
11 − 8	16 − 8	14 − 8	15 − 8	12 − 8
15 − 8	9 − 8	13 − 8	11 − 8	17 − 8
10 − 8	14 − 8	12 − 8	8 − 8	16 − 8

Number of Problems: 30   Number Correct: _____   Time to complete: ____ min.

Skill:

Subtraction -9

11 - 9	17 - 9	9 - 9	14 - 9	18 - 9
10 - 9	13 - 9	16 - 9	12 - 9	15 - 9
9 - 9	16 - 9	11 - 9	13 - 9	17 - 9
15 - 9	10 - 9	18 - 9	14 - 9	12 - 9
10 - 9	17 - 9	11 - 9	18 - 9	15 - 9
12 - 9	16 - 9	14 - 9	10 - 9	13 - 9

Number of Problems: 30   Number Correct: _____   Time to complete: ___ min.

Name: _____

Skill:

Picture Subtraction

Start With	Take Away	What's Left?

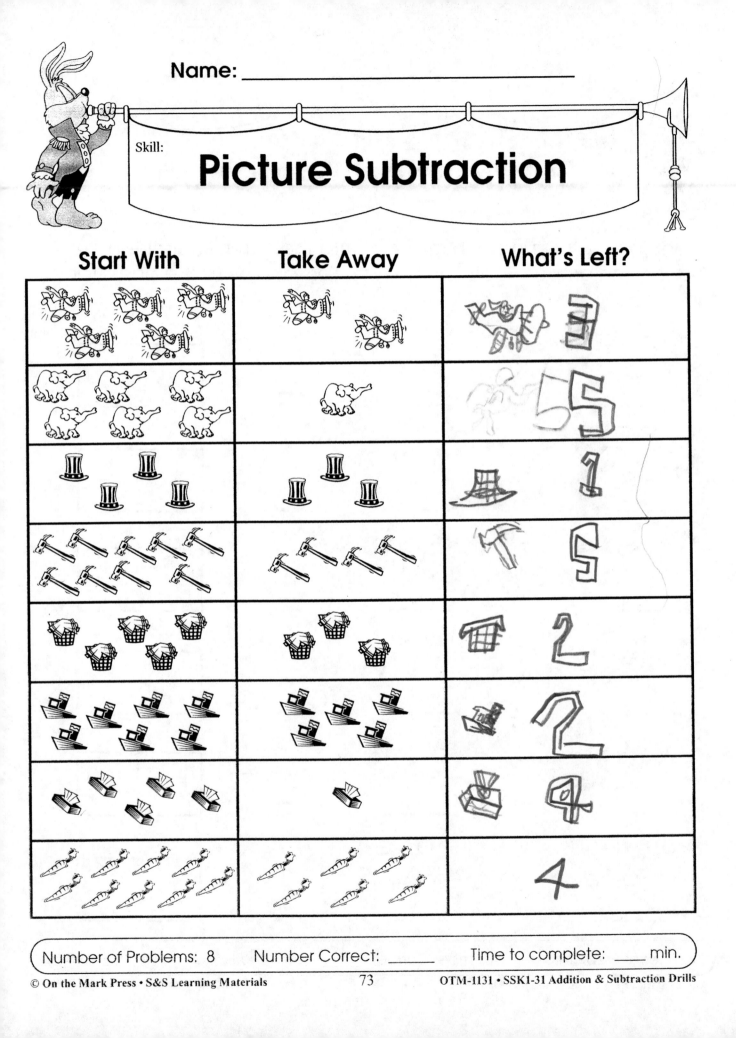

Number of Problems: 8   Number Correct: _____   Time to complete: ____ min.

© On the Mark Press • S&S Learning Materials   73   OTM-1131 • SSK1-31 Addition & Subtraction Drills

Subtraction Sentences

Count the pictures in each group. Write the number on the line under each group. Subtract the numbers and write the answer in the box.

_____   −   _____   =

_____   −   _____   =

_____   −   _____   =

_____   −   _____   =

_____   −   _____   =

_____   −   _____   =

Number of Problems: 6   Number Correct: _____   Time to complete: ____ min.

Name: _____

Skill:

Quick Subtraction Drill

Solve the problems inside the baby dino, then color each one.

Number of Problems: 15   Number Correct: _____   Time to complete: ____ min.

© On the Mark Press • S&S Learning Materials   75   OTM-1131 • SSK1-31 Addition & Subtraction Drills

Skill: _____

Rocket Ship Math

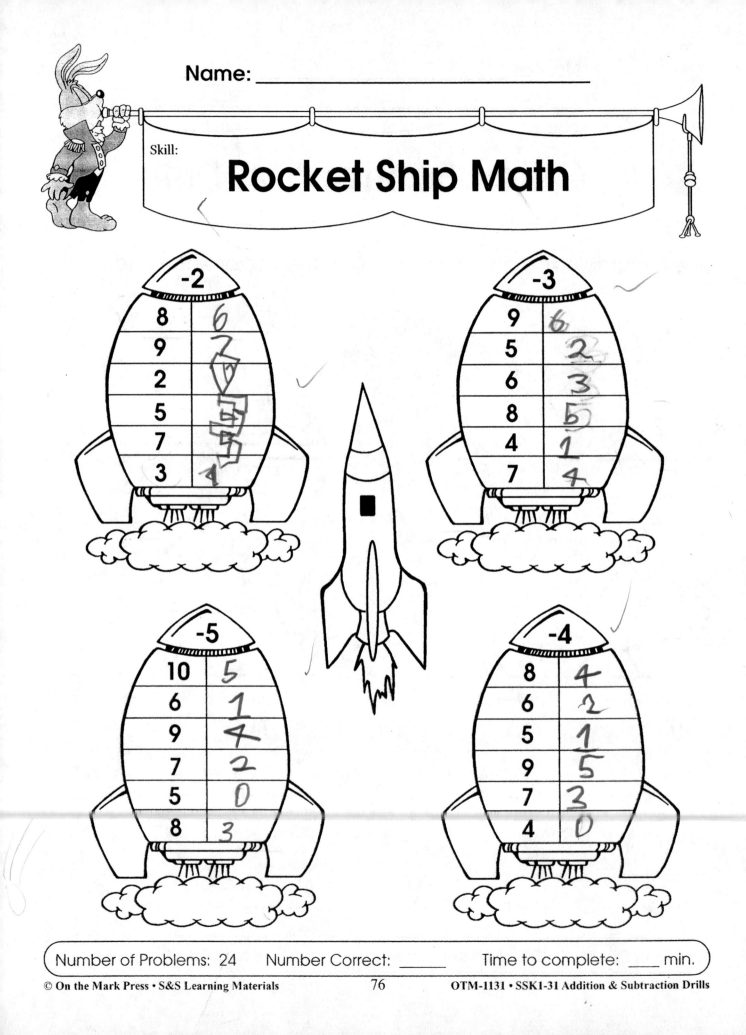

-2

8	6
9	7
2	0
5	3
7	5
3	1

-3

9	6
5	2
6	3
8	5
4	1
7	4

-5

10	5
6	1
9	4
7	2
5	0
8	3

-4

8	4
6	2
5	1
9	5
7	3
4	0

Number of Problems: 24   Number Correct: _____   Time to complete: ____ min.

Skill:

Float the Boats

Fill the blank with the correct numeral to keep your boat afloat.

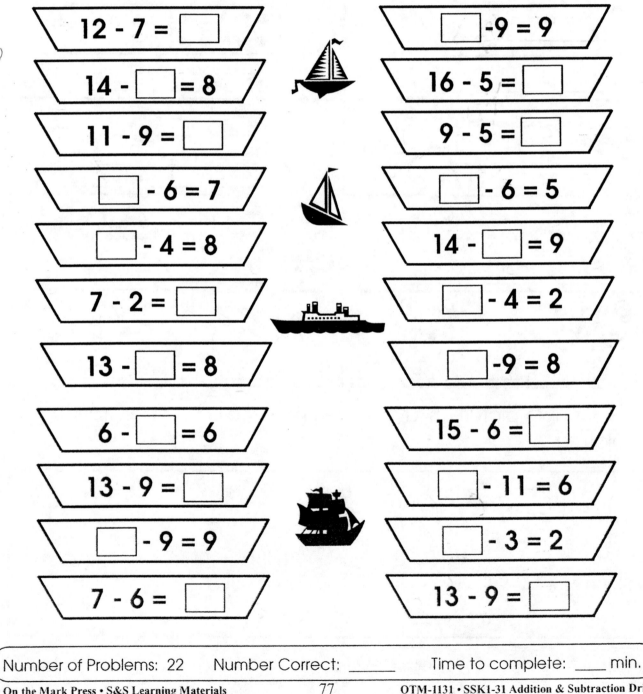

12 - 7 = ☐

14 - ☐ = 8

11 - 9 = ☐

☐ - 6 = 7

☐ - 4 = 8

7 - 2 = ☐

13 - ☐ = 8

6 - ☐ = 6

13 - 9 = ☐

☐ - 9 = 9

7 - 6 = ☐

☐ - 9 = 9

16 - 5 = ☐

9 - 5 = ☐

☐ - 6 = 5

14 - ☐ = 9

☐ - 4 = 2

☐ - 9 = 8

15 - 6 = ☐

☐ - 11 = 6

☐ - 3 = 2

13 - 9 = ☐

Number of Problems: 22   Number Correct: _____   Time to complete: ____ min.

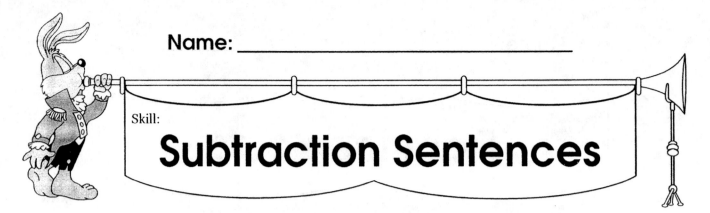

Name: _____

Skill:

Subtraction Sentences

Write a number sentence that matches each picture.

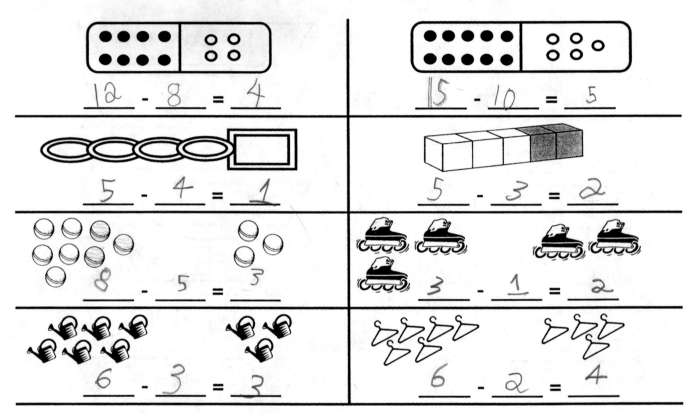

12 - 8 = 4

15 - 10 = 5

5 - 4 = 1

5 - 3 = 2

8 - 5 = 3

3 - 1 = 2

6 - 3 = 3

6 - 2 = 4

Draw your own picture. Have someone write a number story for your picture.

8 ⊞ - ⊞ = ⊞2

Number of Problems: 8   Number Correct: _____   Time to complete: ____ min.

Name: _____

Quick Subtraction Practice

8 − 1 **7**	4 − 2 **2**	8 − 5 **3**	6 − 2 **4**	7 − 7 **0**
5 − 4 **1**	8 − 0 **8**	7 − 4 **3**	8 − 4 **4**	6 − 3 **3**
5 − 2 **3**	6 − 6 **0**	7 − 2 **5**	8 − 3 **5**	7 − 6 **1**
5 − 5 **0**	7 − 1 **6**	4 − 2 **2**	6 − 4 **2**	6 − 0 **6**
9 − 2 **7**	8 − 1 **7**	3 − 2 **1**	9 − 6 **3**	3 − 3 **0**
3 − 1 **2**	6 − 5 **1**	9 − 5 **4**	7 − 7 **0**	8 − 7 **1**

Number of Problems: 30   Number Correct: _____   Time to complete: ____ min.

Name: _____

Skill: Two Digit Subtraction

No Regrouping

23 − 2	17 − 7	12 − 10	19 − 6	13 − 2
15 − 4	14 − 10	19 − 17	18 − 6	63 − 40
27 − 5	38 − 15	77 − 11	63 − 31	87 − 35
16 − 4	42 − 10	80 − 50	93 − 33	76 − 51
14 − 2	48 − 26	84 − 51	64 − 30	67 − 46
18 − 5	59 − 37	15 − 6	17 − 9	15 − 9

Number of Problems: 30   Number Correct: _____   Time to complete: ____ min.

Name: _____

Skill: Two Digit Subtraction
No Regrouping

61 - 41	80 - 62	98 - 34	69 - 46	70 - 30
88 - 62	47 - 27	69 - 36	98 - 41	26 - 24
88 - 32	39 - 26	87 - 45	19 - 15	78 - 43
67 - 52	95 - 43	38 - 25	82 - 51	77 - 45
86 - 21	36 - 33	59 - 37	15 - 10	77 - 64
79 - 22	31 - 10	55 - 11	93 - 33	48 - 26

Number of Problems: 30   Number Correct: _____   Time to complete: ____ min.

Name: _____

Two Digit Subtraction
With Regrouping

12	16	14	11	10
− 7	− 9	− 7	− 6	− 9

15	12	17	19	13
− 6	− 3	− 8	− 10	− 8

14	13	18	10	17
− 8	− 7	− 8	− 6	− 12

18	12	11	15	25
− 9	− 9	− 5	− 9	− 9

13	17	16	12	15
− 4	− 9	− 9	− 7	− 9

10	14	18	11	14
− 7	− 8	− 9	− 7	− 5

Number of Problems: 30   Number Correct: _____   Time to complete: ____ min.

Name: _____

Skill: Two Digit Subtraction
With Regrouping

26 - 18	60 - 27	33 - 26	67 - 49	82 - 45
85 - 36	61 - 29	98 - 39	24 - 17	31 - 15
74 - 58	66 - 18	91 - 49	73 - 57	40 - 23
51 - 42	34 - 27	95 - 46	87 - 58	21 - 16
92 - 36	76 - 59	53 - 28	41 - 28	59 - 34
43 - 18	52 - 44	97 - 48	50 - 25	73 - 27

Number of Problems: 30   Number Correct: _____   Time to complete: ____ min.

Skill: Two Digit Subtraction

With Regrouping   No Regrouping

28	56	53	43	91
- 19	- 36	- 46	- 40	- 24

42	77	77	65	67
- 33	- 34	- 11	- 46	- 46

54	57	59	76	62
- 46	- 48	- 37	- 51	- 49

26	93	73	87	81
- 18	- 33	- 64	- 35	- 72

60	81	67	80	52
- 37	- 51	- 49	- 50	- 43

33	75	67	86	42
- 26	- 52	- 46	- 55	- 33

Number of Problems: 30   Number Correct: _____   Time to complete: ____ min.

Name: _____

Word Problems

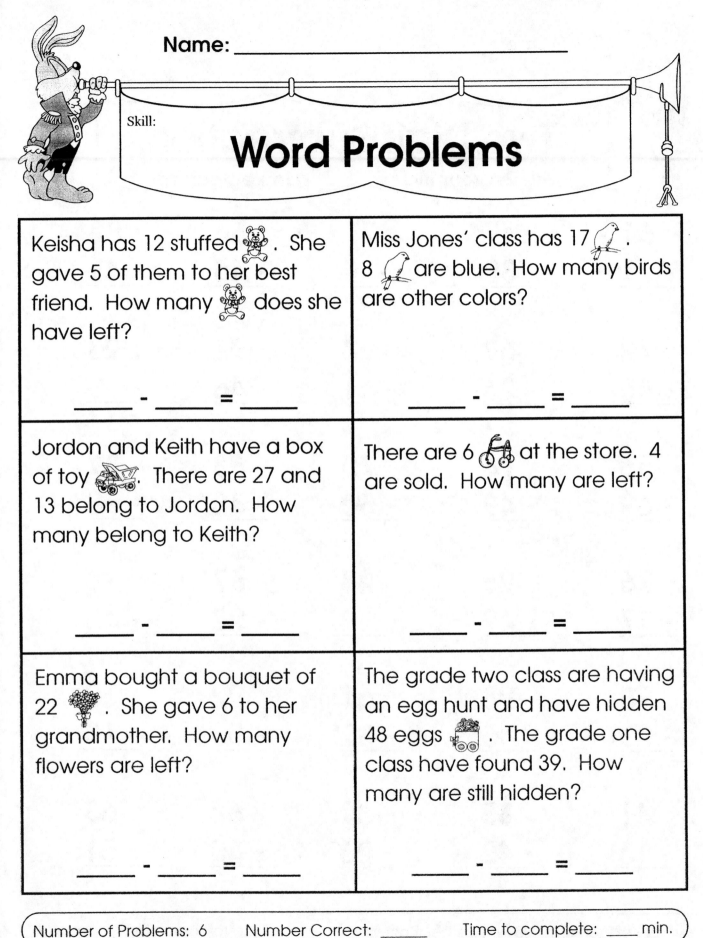

Keisha has 12 stuffed 🧸. She gave 5 of them to her best friend. How many 🧸 does she have left?

_____ - _____ = _____

Miss Jones' class has 17 🐦. 8 🐦 are blue. How many birds are other colors?

_____ - _____ = _____

Jordon and Keith have a box of toy 🚚. There are 27 and 13 belong to Jordon. How many belong to Keith?

_____ - _____ = _____

There are 6 🛺 at the store. 4 are sold. How many are left?

_____ - _____ = _____

Emma bought a bouquet of 22 💐. She gave 6 to her grandmother. How many flowers are left?

_____ - _____ = _____

The grade two class are having an egg hunt and have hidden 48 eggs 🥚. The grade one class have found 39. How many are still hidden?

_____ - _____ = _____

Number of Problems: 6   Number Correct: _____   Time to complete: _____ min.

Name: _____

Skill:

Two Digit Subtraction

With Regrouping   **No Regrouping**

61 − 21	47 − 30	77 − 9	54 − 46	83 − 41
72 − 46	69 − 26	98 − 61	91 − 46	93 − 33
86 − 69	74 − 49	70 − 50	58 − 40	87 − 58
76 − 17	95 − 49	28 − 9	67 − 22	78 − 45
98 − 23	98 − 45	61 − 32	92 − 56	19 − 10
41 − 13	85 − 42	39 − 26	64 − 40	63 − 51

Number of Problems: 30   Number Correct: _____   Time to complete: ____ min.

Name: _____

Skill: _____

Word Problems

There were 7 children outside playing. 4 of them had to leave early. How many were left?

_____ - _____ = _____

The clown at Madison's party blew up 12 balloons. 5 of them were broken by Madison's puppy. How many were left?

_____ - _____ = _____

Keisha's aquarium has too many fish. She counted them and there are 27. She gave 12 to her brother. How many are left?

_____ - _____ = _____

Number of Problems: 3   Number Correct: _____   Time to complete: ____ min.

Skill:

Two Digit Subtraction

99 − 65	98 − 77	78 − 41	64 − 31	37 − 25
85 − 63	88 − 56	28 − 15	75 − 42	88 − 22
76 − 51	73 − 52	61 − 30	65 − 32	93 − 52
82 − 31	85 − 64	95 − 62	74 − 44	36 − 16
94 − 50	78 − 31	39 − 12	58 − 35	43 − 22
56 − 22	85 − 73	86 − 51	67 − 32	75 − 50

Number of Problems: 30   Number Correct: _____   Time to complete: ____ min.

The bird watching club saw 109 birds on Saturday and 89 birds on Sunday. How many more were seen on Saturday?

109 - 89 = _____

The astronomy class kept track of how many stars they saw. One night they saw 876. The next night they saw 342 stars. How many more were seen the first night?

_____ - _____ = _____

The stamp club sent out newsletters each week. Last year they used 64 packages of paper. This year they used 117 packages. How many more were used this year?

_____ - _____ = _____

120 paint brushes were bought for the art class. 73 brushes were used. How many are left?

_____ - _____ = _____

Number of Problems: 4   Number Correct: _____   Time to complete: _____ min.

© On the Mark Press • S&S Learning Materials   89   OTM-1131 • SSK1-31 Addition & Subtraction Drills

Name: _____

Skill:
More Rocket Ship Subtraction

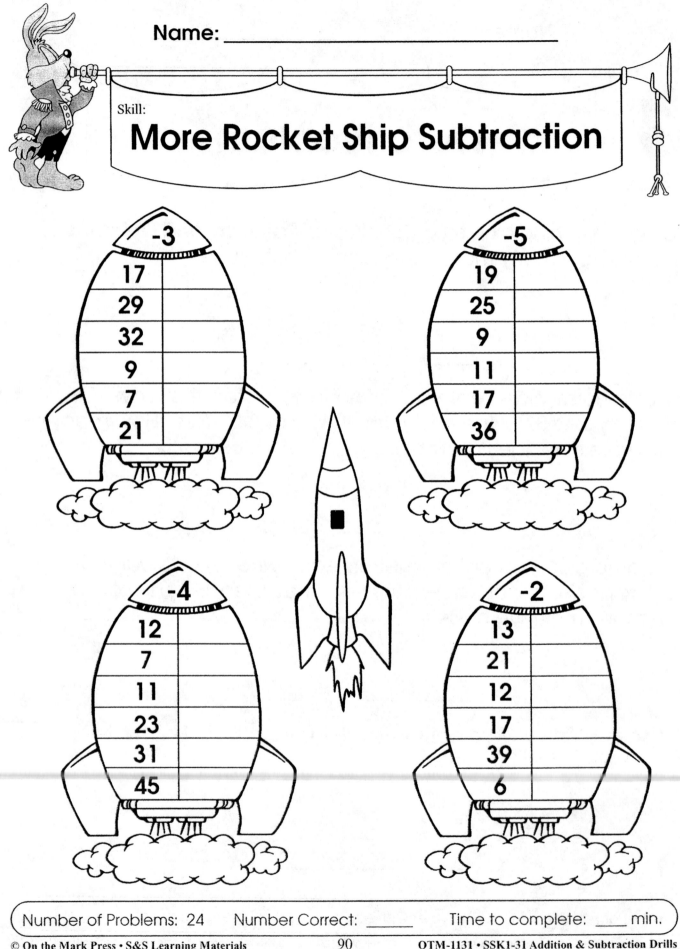

-3

17	
29	
32	
9	
7	
21	

-5

19	
25	
9	
11	
17	
36	

-4

12	
7	
11	
23	
31	
45	

-2

13	
21	
12	
17	
39	
6	

Number of Problems: 24   Number Correct: _____   Time to complete: ____ min.

Skill:

Mixed Subtraction

13 − 9	29 − 7	14 − 8	85 − 41	11 − 6
12 − 8	75 − 52	13 − 6	99 − 35	10 − 1
16 − 7	66 − 27	15 − 8	39 − 38	13 − 8
10 − 3	59 − 26	15 − 9	49 − 14	17 − 9
13 − 5	16 − 16	15 − 2	55 − 37	10 − 9
13 − 3	61 − 40	17 − 10	74 − 42	12 − 7

Number of Problems: 30   Number Correct: _____   Time to complete: ____ min.

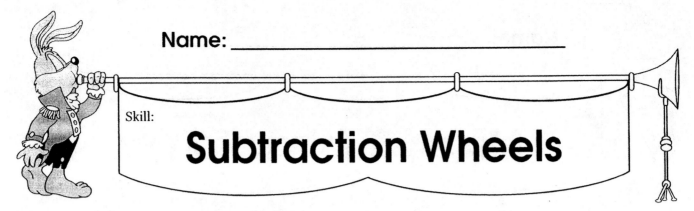

Skill:

Subtraction Wheels

Subtract the number in the middle from each number in turn.
Then write your answer in the blank.

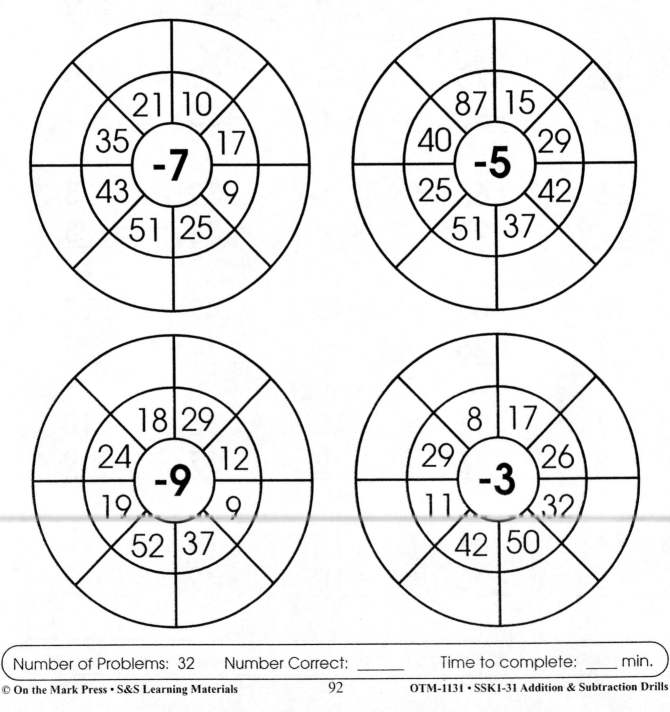

Number of Problems: 32   Number Correct: _____   Time to complete: ____ min.

Skill:

Subtraction - More Practice

91	73	50	97	52
- 59	- 47	- 35	- 38	- 34

24	85	86	95	66
- 7	- 56	- 59	- 56	- 28

67	28	87	33	87
- 44	- 17	- 35	- 22	- 54

56	76	67	27	69
- 31	- 75	- 24	- 16	- 54

98	34	29	99	87
- 47	- 27	- 12	- 66	- 29

92	53	63	61	21
- 26	- 18	- 14	- 29	- 6

Number of Problems: 30   Number Correct: _____   Time to complete: ____ min.

Name: _____

Skill:

Bubble Subtraction

$$\begin{array}{r} 9 \\ -\ 3 \\ \hline \end{array}$$

16 - 8 = ____

$$\begin{array}{r} 27 \\ -\ 9 \\ \hline \end{array}$$

$$\begin{array}{r} 38 \\ -\ 16 \\ \hline \end{array}$$

$$\begin{array}{r} 12 \\ -\ 7 \\ \hline \end{array}$$

$$\begin{array}{r} 68 \\ -\ 49 \\ \hline \end{array}$$

34 - 9 = ____

$$\begin{array}{r} 72 \\ -\ 56 \\ \hline \end{array}$$

$$\begin{array}{r} 29 \\ -\ 13 \\ \hline \end{array}$$

$$\begin{array}{r} 32 \\ -\ 16 \\ \hline \end{array}$$

$$\begin{array}{r} 13 \\ -\ 8 \\ \hline \end{array}$$

42 - 24 = ____

Number of Problems: 12   Number Correct: _____   Time to complete: ____ min.

Skill:

Three Digit Subtraction

No Regrouping

335 − 104	180 − 100	169 − 30	975 − 130	152 − 112
676 − 123	144 − 20	130 − 120	152 − 100	251 − 140
625 − 212	569 − 328	894 − 451	745 − 302	492 − 160
552 − 521	474 − 221	145 − 120	649 − 145	452 − 104
234 − 221	593 − 72	244 − 100	933 − 312	969 − 363
895 − 431	587 − 322	698 − 513	176 − 133	789 − 488

Number of Problems: 30   Number Correct: _____   Time to complete: ____ min.

Skill:

Three Digit Subtraction
No Regrouping

973 - 953	556 - 215	596 - 293	880 - 220	187 - 135
695 - 393	492 - 330	272 - 240	659 - 314	817 - 215
274 - 213	949 - 224	999 - 674	871 - 301	636 - 120
858 - 235	695 - 133	673 - 432	356 - 153	857 - 746
889 - 834	746 - 233	958 - 908	923 - 912	372 - 361

Number of Problems: 25   Number Correct: _____   Time to complete: ____ min.

Three Digit Subtraction

With Regrouping

Skill:

509 - 482	251 - 180	412 - 225	526 - 484	306 - 178
533 - 184	385 - 168	311 - 280	182 - 135	860 - 638
283 - 136	830 - 246	282 - 105	991 - 264	510 - 366
382 - 194	328 - 229	224 - 136	772 - 313	806 - 273
700 - 305	910 - 328	602 - 519	934 - 665	707 - 257

Number of Problems: 25   Number Correct: _____   Time to complete: _____ min.

Skill:

What's Missing?

$$
\begin{array}{r}
7\ 5 \\
-\ 5\ \square \\
\hline
\square\ 2
\end{array}
\qquad
\begin{array}{r}
6\ 1 \\
-\ \square\ \square \\
\hline
1\ 4
\end{array}
\qquad
\begin{array}{r}
4\ \square \\
-\ 1\ 1 \\
\hline
\square\ 7
\end{array}
\qquad
\begin{array}{r}
8\ 2 \\
-\ 3\ \square \\
\hline
\square\ 1
\end{array}
$$

$$
\begin{array}{r}
\square\ \square \\
-\ 1\ 5 \\
\hline
1\ 0
\end{array}
\qquad
\begin{array}{r}
\square\ \square \\
-\ 1\ 0 \\
\hline
6
\end{array}
\qquad
\begin{array}{r}
\square\ 6 \\
-\ 3\ \square \\
\hline
3\ 3
\end{array}
\qquad
\begin{array}{r}
\square\ \square \\
-\ 7\ 3 \\
\hline
1\ 1
\end{array}
$$

$$
\begin{array}{r}
2\ \square \\
-\ \ 9 \\
\hline
1\ 6
\end{array}
\qquad
\begin{array}{r}
8\ 9 \\
-\ \square\ \square \\
\hline
3\ 7
\end{array}
\qquad
\begin{array}{r}
4\ 4 \\
-\ \square\ \square \\
\hline
3\ 3
\end{array}
\qquad
\begin{array}{r}
\square\ \square \\
-\ 1\ 5 \\
\hline
1\ 1
\end{array}
$$

$$
\begin{array}{r}
1\ 3 \\
-\ \square\ \square \\
\hline
3
\end{array}
\qquad
\begin{array}{r}
9\ \square \\
-\ \square\ 2 \\
\hline
1\ 2
\end{array}
\qquad
\begin{array}{r}
\square\ \square \\
-\ 1\ 6 \\
\hline
3\ 0
\end{array}
\qquad
\begin{array}{r}
6\ 3 \\
-\ 4\ 1 \\
\hline
\square\ \square
\end{array}
$$

$$
\begin{array}{r}
8\ 0 \\
-\ \square\ \square \\
\hline
2\ 7
\end{array}
\qquad
\begin{array}{r}
9\ 6 \\
-\ \square\ \square \\
\hline
3\ 3
\end{array}
\qquad
\begin{array}{r}
\square\ 6 \\
-\ 1\ \square \\
\hline
2\ 1
\end{array}
\qquad
\begin{array}{r}
4\ 1 \\
-\ \square\ \square \\
\hline
2\ 5
\end{array}
$$

Number of Problems: 20   Number Correct: _____   Time to complete: ____ min.

Name: _____

You're a Star!

14
- 8

20
- 10

69
- 41

74
- 50

93
- 60

71
- 28

28
- 7

84
- 61

55
- 30

54
- 49

21
- 14

50
- 18

67
- 19

50
- 22

94
- 33

Number of Problems: 15   Number Correct: _____   Time to complete: ____ min.

Name: _____

Skill:
Grocery Bag Subtraction

Write three different number sentences that will give you the correct answer. The first one is done for you.

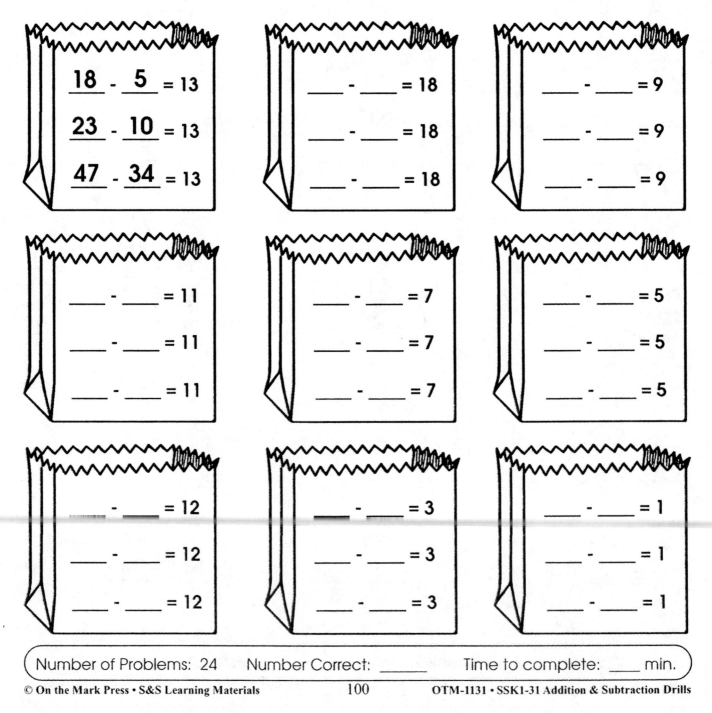

__18__ - __5__ = 13	___ - ___ = 18	___ - ___ = 9
__23__ - __10__ = 13	___ - ___ = 18	___ - ___ = 9
__47__ - __34__ = 13	___ - ___ = 18	___ - ___ = 9

___ - ___ = 11	___ - ___ = 7	___ - ___ = 5
___ - ___ = 11	___ - ___ = 7	___ - ___ = 5
___ - ___ = 11	___ - ___ = 7	___ - ___ = 5

___ - ___ = 12	___ - ___ = 3	___ - ___ = 1
___ - ___ = 12	___ - ___ = 3	___ - ___ = 1
___ - ___ = 12	___ - ___ = 3	___ - ___ = 1

Number of Problems: 24   Number Correct: _____   Time to complete: ____ min.

Name: _____

Skill: _____

Word Problems

Last year, a farmer grew 3 207 🎃 . This year, he had 5 294 🎃 . How many more 🎃 did he have?

_____ - _____ = _____

The SPCA had 39 🐱 and kittens to give away. They found homes for 14 of them. How many 🐱 were left?

_____ - _____ = _____

Emma's mother baked 🍪 for the bake sale. She made 480 🍪 . While putting the cookies in bags, Emma found 27 broken ones. How many 🍪 are unbroken?

_____ - _____ = _____

Jordan and his friend went 🎿 . 42 people rode the chair lift to the top of the ski hill. 19 people skied down. How many people were left?

_____ - _____ = _____

Number of Problems: 4   Number Correct: _____   Time to complete: ____ min.

Mixed Subtraction

Skill:

No Regrouping

49 − 44	6 − 3	76 − 32	372 − 122	79 − 32
637 − 32	88 − 37	54 − 52	353 − 211	67 − 35
889 − 173	699 − 673	48 − 35	75 − 50	534 − 31
189 − 3	28 − 4	25 − 5	794 − 520	86 − 15
256 − 212	8 − 4	23 − 0	519 − 518	3 − 1
667 − 427	86 − 32	71 − 1	2 − 0	794 − 373

Number of Problems: 30   Number Correct: _____   Time to complete: ____ min.

Mixed Subtraction
No Regrouping

Skill:

698 − 615	43 − 11	866 − 300	85 − 20	4 − 2
56 − 24	464 − 443	28 − 7	137 − 6	4 − 1
729 − 519	19 − 12	608 − 208	76 − 32	927 − 522
88 − 71	748 − 630	38 − 16	489 − 170	88 − 20
478 − 441	94 − 33	527 − 323	15 − 5	699 − 68
2 − 0	599 − 583	6 − 0	371 − 230	84 − 81

Number of Problems: 30   Number Correct: _____   Time to complete: ____ min.

Skill:

Banner Subtraction

| 65
- 52 | 13
- 0 | 93
- 40 | 86
- 31 |

| 87
- 17 | 59
- 46 | 49
- 43 | 39
- 18 |

| 13
- 2 | 17
- 5 | 65
- 44 | 68
- 18 |

| 69
- 41 | 93
- 60 | 74
- 50 | 38
- 5 |

Number of Problems: 16   Number Correct: _____   Time to complete: ____ min.

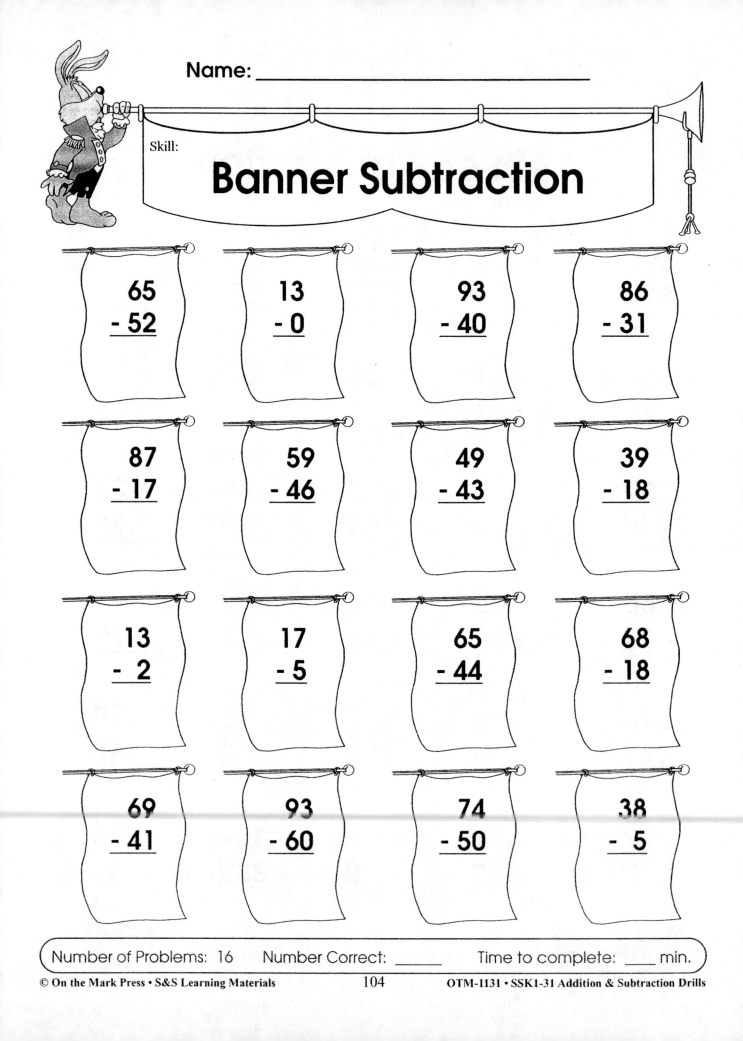

Skill:

Subtraction with Decimals

With Regrouping   No Regrouping

3.63	3.90	5.90	0.31	2.34
- 2.08	- 2.05	- 3.68	- 0.06	- 1.72

9.19	8.36	4.46	4.00	1.9
- 4.91	- 1.03	- 4.31	- 1.06	- 0.8

8.52	4.65	9.38	1.09	5.31
- 8.08	- 0.43	- 1.26	- 0.27	- 2.97

5.89	6.12	2.69	5.09	5.24
- 1.82	- 3.65	- 0.45	- 4.31	- 1.75

0.86	1.40	1.92	0.68	4.55
- 0.59	- 0.01	- 0.45	- 0.49	- 1.83

9.57	7.12	9.22	9.13	1.66
- 2.27	- 4.05	- 8.22	- 1.12	- 0.43

Number of Problems: 30   Number Correct: _____   Time to complete: _____ min.

Skill:

Subtraction with Decimals

With Regrouping   No Regrouping

72.58	26.48	83.43	78.92
- 1.98	- 5.98	- 1.66	- 16.96

0.88	1.37	4.67	9.47
- 0.81	- 1.00	- 4.07	- 2.54

65.68	4.64	97.72	46.31
- 32.56	- 3.56	- 34.49	- 24.08

6.46	8.01	2.28	3.25
- 5.01	- 3.00	- 0.68	- 0.09

9.17	23.30	2.33	54.62
- 7.73	- 15.26	- 0.30	- 32.56

Number of Problems: 20   Number Correct: _____   Time to complete: ____ min.

Name: _____

Subtraction Review
One and Two Digit Numbers

89 − 35	9 − 1	15 − 9	99 − 95	18 − 14
48 − 30	43 − 33	60 − 21	14 − 11	2 − 0
95 − 43	12 − 8	86 − 16	59 − 31	67 − 9
58 − 57	16 − 6	54 − 10	48 − 8	45 − 14
91 − 14	94 − 90	7 − 6	47 − 16	17 − 8
76 − 27	55 − 19	23 − 15	24 − 11	86 − 35

Number of Problems: 30   Number Correct: _____   Time to complete: ____ min.

Subtraction Review
One and Two Digit Numbers

Skill:

16 - 5	69 - 12	91 - 66	60 - 40	78 - 7
61 - 26	30 - 6	3 - 2	90 - 27	8 - 2
56 - 42	22 - 6	76 - 26	38 - 8	38 - 27
74 - 12	86 - 70	13 - 4	62 - 19	2 - 1
99 - 21	10 - 3	32 - 9	36 - 12	42 - 23
17 - 4	71 - 59	81 - 16	65 - 27	65 - 10

Number of Problems: 30   Number Correct: _____   Time to complete: ____ min.

Subtraction Review
Two and Three Digit Numbers

Skill:

906 - 729	427 - 217	89 - 35	15 - 9	788 - 430
846 - 176	529 - 144	274 - 19	99 - 95	844 - 558
74 - 54	994 - 13	18 - 14	793 - 786	48 - 30
458 - 421	43 - 33	837 - 81	60 - 21	14 - 11
684 - 261	95 - 43	690 - 579	86 - 16	325 - 195
65 - 61	574 - 91	59 - 31	604 - 545	67 - 9

Number of Problems: 30   Number Correct: _____   Time to complete: ____ min.

Skill:

Mixed Review

16	0.31	37	9	33
− 10	− 0.06	− 9	− 1	− 10

43	587	57	0.02	6.46
− 28	− 144	− 33	− 0.01	− 5.00

8.01	0.12	404	2	37.06
− 3.68	− 0.07	− 159	− 0	− 10.85

47.92	61	12	651	53
− 17.89	− 55	− 8	− 200	− 12

7	0.24	20	77	2.28
− 6	− 0.12	− 10	− 48	− 0.68

38	601	3.25	16	46
− 1	− 51	− 0.09	− 6	− 33

Number of Problems: 30   Number Correct: _____   Time to complete: ____ min.

Skill:

Two Digit Subtraction

81 - 44	49 - 7	63 - 8	85 - 1	43 - 14
54 - 49	70 - 58	19 - 6	41 - 35	57 - 1
23 - 22	89 - 55	80 - 35	82 - 38	13 - 11
56 - 6	88 - 83	50 - 11	16 - 3	31 - 30
19 - 13	62 - 10	25 - 17	58 - 1	40 - 6
13 - 4	68 - 18	90 - 65	75 - 68	85 - 76

Number of Problems: 30   Number Correct: _____   Time to complete: ____ min.

Three Digit Subtraction

Skill:

421 - 27	911 - 8	572 - 399	858 - 451	982 - 244
175 - 3	568 - 167	956 - 849	928 - 914	375 - 224
452 - 241	601 - 98	959 - 934	533 - 336	995 - 223
526 - 211	729 - 186	406 - 137	927 - 458	303 - 216
162 - 152	247 - 129	244 - 198	715 - 712	586 - 466
596 - 399	222 - 167	700 - 146	591 - 263	965 - 931

Number of Problems: 30   Number Correct: _____   Time to complete: ____ min.

Skill: _____

Word Problems

Keisha bought 12 candy apples. She gave her 4 sisters each one.
How many does she have left?

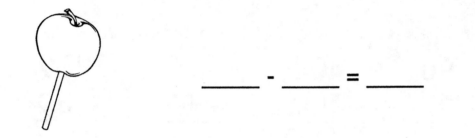

_____ - _____ = _____

Carrie found 13 books under her bed. She misplaced 3 of them.
How many does she have left?

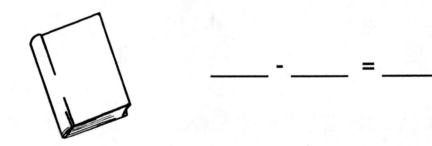

_____ - _____ = _____

Todd and Josh went fishing. They caught 8 fish. They put 6 back in
the water. How many did they keep?

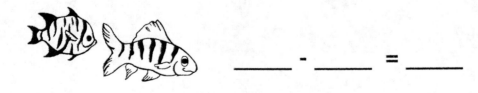

_____ - _____ = _____

Number of Problems: 3   Number Correct: _____   Time to complete: _____ min.

Mixed Subtraction

374 − 103	80 − 35	415 − 299	150 − 31	82 − 38
577 − 548	90 − 27	404 − 159	70 − 63	159 − 49
73 − 28	611 − 504	94 − 59	319 − 221	39 − 15
55 − 11	966 − 224	23 − 7	860 − 448	8 − 7
540 − 152	54 − 37	89 − 78	555 − 356	271 − 233

Number of Problems: 25   Number Correct: _____   Time to complete: ____ min.

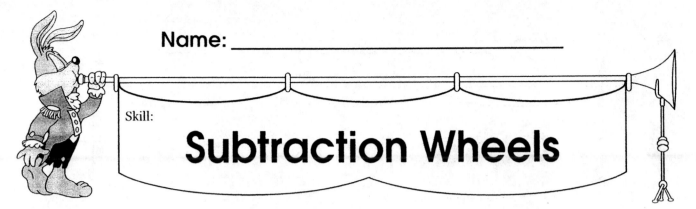

Name: _____

Skill: _____

Subtraction Wheels

Subtract the number in the middle from each number in turn.
Then write your answer in the blank.

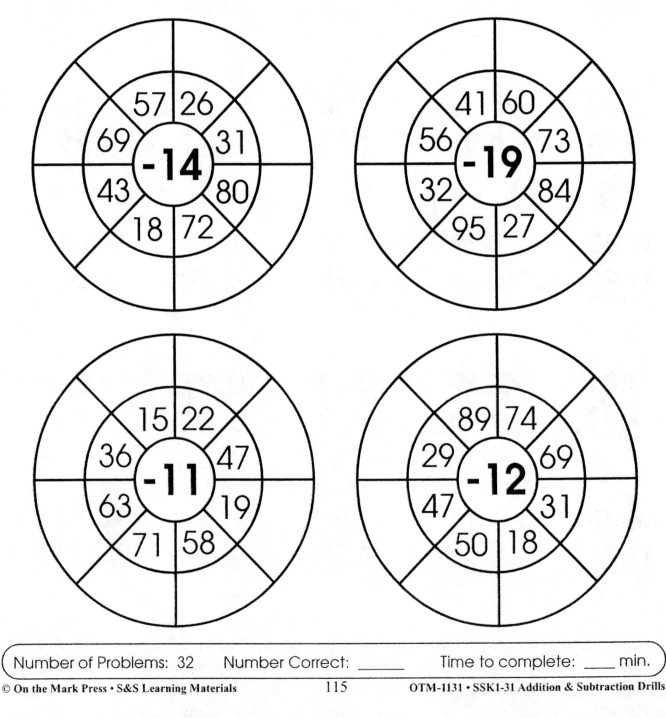

Number of Problems: 32   Number Correct: _____   Time to complete: ____ min.

© On the Mark Press • S&S Learning Materials   115   OTM-1131 • SSK1-31 Addition & Subtraction Drills

Name: _____

Skill:
Subtracting Decimals

36.67 − 23.69	7.88 − 7.67	37.74 − 9.14	9.07 − 8.53	96.38 − 91.91
8.80 − 0.94	75.08 − 8.62	4.36 − 1.83	36.34 − 34.03	0.81 − 0.20
82.52 − 31.26	8.89 − 5.69	89.76 − 41.28	6.35 − 3.29	59.81 − 57.02
3.84 − 2.48	42.59 − 3.15	3.24 − 1.15	81.95 − 69.84	1.27 − 0.84
84.38 − 31.81	5.18 − 0.59	17.95 − 4.75	5.67 − 0.69	98.50 − 16.67

Number of Problems: 25   Number Correct: _____   Time to complete: ____ min.

Skill: _____

Word Problems

Emily bought 3 cans of paint. She used 1 can to paint her room.
How many cans of paint are left?

_____ - _____ = _____

On Tuesday, 431 people rode the train. On Wednesday, 138 rode
the train. How many more people rode the train on Tuesday?

_____ - _____ = _____

The beekeeper harvested 93 containers of honey. She sold 36 on
Saturday and 41 on Sunday. How many are containers of honey
are left?

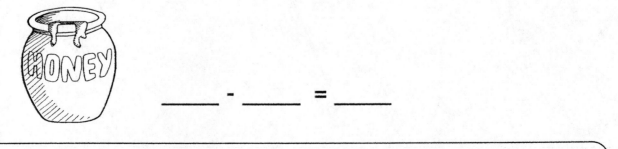

_____ - _____ = _____

Number of Problems: 3   Number Correct: _____   Time to complete: ____ min.

Name: _____

Skill: _____

The Sky's the Limit

Once you have answered each problem, color the kite.

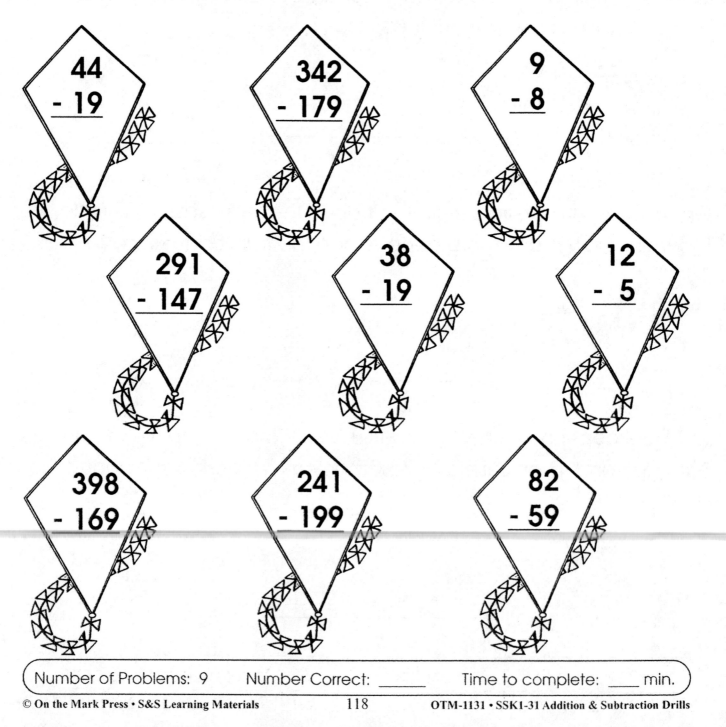

44
- 19

342
- 179

9
- 8

291
- 147

38
- 19

12
- 5

398
- 169

241
- 199

82
- 59

Number of Problems: 9   Number Correct: _____   Time to complete: ____ min.

Skill:

Four Digit Subtraction

With Regrouping   No Regrouping

4969	9063	2933	4764
- 1397	- 4882	- 1341	- 2601

5174	9359	7872	7651
- 3442	- 2871	- 4230	- 5450

7589	3875	7485	6750
- 6206	- 1556	- 5183	- 3030

5257	9378	5828	3964
- 4271	- 3142	- 2364	- 2842

4295	6271	6581	6549
- 2755	- 3230	- 2556	- 4069

4958	6389	8591	7688
- 3121	- 3383	- 2303	- 5159

Number of Problems: 24   Number Correct: _____   Time to complete: ____ min.

Name: _____

0.88 - 0.10	5.55 - 3.56	10.00 - 3.47	1.26 - 0.97	3.15 - 1.73
0.30 - 0.09	4.56 - 3.06	37.57 - 1.62	1.58 - 0.44	0.63 - 0.44
2.60 - 2.41	3.10 - 0.04	0.38 - 0.15	5.44 - 2.10	2.09 - 0.76
7.95 - 1.38	98.75 - 34.59	1.61 - 1.56	4.38 - 2.96	0.34 - 0.08
40.51 - 7.85	9.79 - 2.50	6.69 - 2.58	0.13 - 0.09	3.80 - 2.48
1.71 - 1.44	9.24 - 7.60	5.05 - 1.22	59.81 - 57.02	0.23 - 0.12

Number of Problems: 30   Number Correct: _____   Time to complete: _____ min.

Certificate

has done an amazing job on

Addition

Keep up the good work!

Teacher

Date

Addition Skills

Work

Well Done!

Certificate

_____

has done an amazing job on

Subtraction

Keep up the good work!

_____
Teacher

_____
Date

Work

Subtraction Skills

Well Done!

Answer Key - *Addition Drills*

Adding with Zero: *(page 3)*

6	7	1	3	4
8	2	5	0	7
1	4	9	6	3
5	0	8	2	9
6	9	2	1	7
0	3	5	8	4

Adding with One: *(page 4)*

7	9	5	10	1
8	6	4	2	3
3	9	5	4	8
2	10	6	9	7
8	4	10	6	3
9	2	7	5	1

Adding with Two: *(page 5)*

7	9	11	4	6
5	3	8	10	2
11	6	9	7	4
8	10	2	5	3
4	8	3	11	10
5	7	9	2	6

Adding with Three: *(page 6)*

4	10	12	8	3
5	9	7	11	6
12	4	3	10	8
6	5	11	7	9
10	5	11	7	3
6	8	12	6	9

Adding with Four: *(page 7)*

4	6	11	9	12
5	8	10	13	7
7	9	12	5	13
6	10	11	4	8
9	11	6	12	7
5	10	4	13	8

Adding with Five: *(page 8)*

11	5	7	6	10
8	12	9	14	13
6	8	13	11	9
10	14	5	12	7
14	10	5	8	12
11	7	6	13	9

Adding with Six: *(page 9)*

15	8	10	13	7
9	12	6	14	11
7	10	15	8	13
11	6	9	14	12
8	13	8	6	12
11	15	9	14	10

Adding with Seven: *(page 10)*

12	10	7	16	8
9	15	13	11	14
7	16	8	9	14
12	10	15	11	13
7	9	16	10	14
8	12	15	11	13

Adding with Eight: *(page 11)*

8	12	14	16	9
17	10	13	15	11
9	16	8	12	13
14	11	15	10	17
11	13	9	8	17
14	16	10	17	12

Adding with Nine: *(page 12)*

10	14	18	15	11
16	12	17	9	13
9	13	12	16	10
18	11	14	17	15
16	10	12	18	9
11	15	13	17	14

Picture Addition: *(page 13)*

5	9	7	11	9	10	11
12						

Addition Sentences: *(page 14)*

5	9	5	9	7	12

Quick Addition Drill: *(page 15)*

5	8	3	7
6	4	5	5
7	7	1	9
7	11	6	

Rocket Ship Math: *(page 16)*

Coloring Sums: *(page 17)*

4	9	10	5	8	10	7
9	6	5	8	8		

Float the Boats: *(page 18)*

7	9	11	2	7	9
11	11	6	5	8	5
4	4	9	8		
7	4	10	4		

Addition Sentences: *(page 19)*

5 + 2 = 7	6 + 3 = 9
1 + 4 = 5	2 + 3 = 5
4 + 4 = 8	3 + 3 = 6
3 + 6 = 9	6 + 4 = 10

Column Addition: *(page 20)*

4	6	5	7	6
8	10	10	13	15
10	5	8	8	24
9	9	12	12	13
11	12	14	16	16

Two Digit Addition - No Regrouping: *(page 21)*

22	27	29	28
25	29	27	25
25	29	29	29
23	23	27	25
26	28	28	29

Two Digit Addition - No Regrouping: *(page 22)*

28	26	37	58
28	35	38	59
28	25	49	38
38	69	68	88
59	39	59	77

Two Digit Addition - With Regrouping: *(page 23)*

20	22	20	21	20
21	23	23	25	28
23	25	22	25	22
21	24	24	22	20
24	20	20	23	20
26	27	21	21	25

Two Digit Addition - With Regrouping/No Regrouping: *(page 24)*

112	66	110	37	89
85	122	62	76	97
95	149	148	28	64
158	127	98	96	115
115	89	54	117	124
63	164	142	117	106

Word Problems: *(page 25)*

9 + 18 = 27
12 + 13 = 25
13 + 12 + 9 = 34
5 + 6 + 2 = 13
3 + 4 = 7
4 + 3 = 7

Two Digit Addition - With Regrouping/No Regrouping: *(page 26)*

91	85	99	171
111	26	79	114
81	99	29	79
72	130	119	134
63	106	78	135
97	66	81	89

Visual Addition: *(page 27)*

7 + 2 + 2 = 11
5 + 4 + 2 = 11

Two Digit Addition - With Regrouping/No Regrouping: *(page 28)*

90	51	87	92
89	49	82	60
29	70	98	99
96	78	76	83
90	87	73	71
87	79	89	95

Picture Puzzles: *(page 29)*

5 + 6 = 11
2 + 1 + 1 = 4
7 + 4 = 11
7 + 6 = 13

More Rocket Ship Math: *(page 30)*

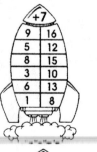

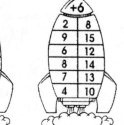

Addition - No Regrouping: *(page 31)*

45	26	28	27	49
36	34	59	33	58
67	27	37	55	57
75	90	79	59	56
57	77	59	54	68
44	49	67	69	79

Addition Wheels: *(page 32)*

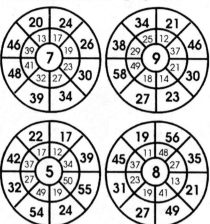

Addition - With Regrouping/No Regrouping: *(page 33)*

29	21	19	6	11
9	13	10	11	20
44	87	48	105	98
95	77	8	25	52
107	116	113	109	35
147	76	94	177	131

Bubble Addition: *(page 34)*

350	312	63	1005
508	316	1152	528
324	333	118	
628	145	40	

Three Digit Addition - With Regrouping/No Regrouping: *(page 35)*

536	389	490	835	796
446	228	342	548	376
318	271	299	939	628
332	821	1539	1059	733
1419	294	1339	472	584
1032	942	1155	1134	707

Two Digit Column Addition: *(page 36)*

83	80	106	160	161
18	36	71	80	37
135	95	138	105	124
43	160	36	170	73
164	91	123	80	147
72	132	148	75	56

Three Digit Column Addition: *(page 37)*

423	864	1491	490
239	1818	321	552
464	383	411	1475
446	375	474	518
1205	664	330	1283

Balloon Addition: *(page 38)*

1146	1220	310
1199	972	1791
224	597	

What's Missing?: *(page 39)*

(39, 12) 42 (17, 52) (26, 14)
21 (50, 10) (38, 14) 87
(83, 48) (26, 5) (48, 36) (16, 10)
(28, 9) 35 9 (17, 50)
79 28 (18, 16) (72, 45)

You're A Star!: *(page 40)*

95	66	37
89	71	15
75	49	108
25	35	87
31	51	41

Grocery Bag Addition: *(page 41)*

Answers may vary as long as the equation equals the sum.

Word Problems: *(page 42)*

23 + 8 = 31
43 + 29 + 74 = 146
23 + 7 + 12 = 42
27 + 29 = 56

Addition - No Regrouping: *(page 43)*

59	85	34	77
29	59	27	68
35	97	39	88
43	88	79	77
51	99	78	45
58	89	69	58

Addition - No Regrouping: *(page 44)*

55	57	79	70
47	39	49	97
78	48	56	48
86	66	85	78
66	28	99	78
75	77	88	99

Column Addition - No Regrouping: *(page 45)*

895	79	819	89
919	99	576	69
76	489	776	66
698	39	88	779

Adding Decimals: *(page 46)*

6.10	5.78	5.12	12.96
9.12	7.72	11.03	3.69
7.65	10.66	6.51	9.10
11.16	14.54	9.60	3.45
4.86	4.14	12.15	7.83
5.41	11.05	13.96	3.72

Three Digit Addition - No Regrouping: *(page 47)*

607	898	385	998
867	449	849	572
596	769	969	985
558	968	343	677
559	498	758	611
769	933	959	567

Three Digit Column Addition - With Regrouping/No Regrouping: *(page 48)*

877	476	616	1054
958	1122	1399	1182
979	2171	554	1334
668	1460	557	1220
2273	2109	1371	2628

Two Digit Addition - With Regrouping: *(page 49)*

41	80	85	55
72	31	58	85
180	114	134	61
125	140	101	152
51	126	181	151
61	30	124	192

Three Digit Addition - With Regrouping: *(page 50)*

573	338	491	919
1470	1071	585	1532
636	663	1094	1208
392	537	1352	335
892	1020	654	1316
1032	923	884	1689

Four Digit Addition - No Regrouping: *(page 51)*

4237	8176	3999	8975
5989	6787	9899	5999
8857	5768	9979	7669
10959	5879	4469	7787
8959	9797	8957	9856
9685	8869	9997	9978

Four Digit Addition - With Regrouping: *(page 52)*

3075	16946	6862	3670
2480	10638	10170	14174
8761	9468	7124	6217
15458	9769	11107	9101
14785	8855	12288	10760
11463	6906	4955	11837

Word Problems: *(page 53)*

$4.50 + $4.50 + $1.25 + $2.25 + $2.25 = $14.75

7 + 3 + 1 + 11 + 5 + 1 = 28

$3.50 + $3.50 + $2.50 + $2.50 = $12.00

623 + 891 = 1514

6 + 3 = 9

Mixed Addition: *(page 54)*

61	390	69	991	101
592	58	482	68	599
60	700	66	956	97
769	145	624	880	45
89	970	165	91	115
34	1320	61	1000	40

Addition Wheels: *(page 55)*

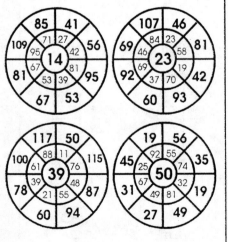

Adding Decimals - With Regrouping/No Regrouping: *(page 56)*

13.06	19.37	2.98	3.67
5.49	2.82	7.61	8.46
8.78	6.81	3.95	10.45
8.30	4.74	3.68	7.35
13.58	9.79	13.18	5.88

Word Problems: *(page 57)*

120 + 85 = 205

41 + 37 + 29 + 23 = 130

280 + 185 = 465

17 + 24 - 41

Review - With Regrouping/No Regrouping: *(page 58)*

70	27	83	100	41
111	69	95	53	89
370	388	499	788	499
239	279	499	985	1000
28	249	100	590	1657
60	98	10	107	975

The Sky's the Limit: *(page 59)*

106	48	42
34	67	33
110	42	96
49	101	38
43	96	48

Four Digit Addition - With Regrouping/No Regouping: *(page 60)*

3085	16946	6862	3670
2480	10638	10170	14174
8761	11468	7124	6217
15458	9769	11107	9101
14785	8855	12288	10760

Answer Key - *Subtraction Drills*

Subtraction -0: *(page 3)*

7	5	8	6	2
1	2	6	0	8
9	1	3	4	6
3	5	7	0	6
4	8	2	1	5
7	9	0	1	8

Subtraction -1: *(page 4)*

6	8	0	2	5
1	4	7	9	3
2	9	3	7	1
8	5	0	2	4
7	2	8	4	9
6	0	3	5	1

Subtraction -2: *(page 5)*

0	2	7	3	1
4	6	8	5	0
6	2	8	7	3
8	4	1	5	0
7	0	4	2	6
5	3	1	8	7

Subtraction -3: *(page 6)*

4	7	3	1	2
1	5	4	7	6
3	0	2	4	7
5	6	1	2	0
3	5	7	4	6
2	0	4	3	1

Subtraction -4: *(page 7)*

6	3	0	5	1
4	6	2	4	3
5	0	6	4	1
3	0	5	2	1
0	4	2	5	3
6	4	2	0	1

Subtraction -5: *(page 8)*

4	7	2	5	0
6	1	3	7	2
0	4	5	1	6
7	1	2	3	5
6	4	5	2	0
3	6	0	3	4

Subtraction -6: *(page 9)*

7	3	0	1	5
2	6	1	4	6
2	5	4	7	3
0	3	7	4	1
5	2	3	5	6
7	0	2	6	3

Subtraction -7: *(page 10)*

4	2	8	5	7
3	6	1	2	9
8	9	5	2	0
4	7	1	6	3
2	9	0	5	8
4	7	1	6	2

Subtraction -8: *(page 11)*

7	5	9	3	1
0	4	2	8	6
2	5	1	0	9
3	8	6	7	4
7	1	5	3	9
2	6	4	0	8

Subtraction -9: *(page 12)*

2	8	0	5	9
1	4	7	3	6
0	7	2	4	8
6	1	9	5	3
1	8	2	9	6
3	7	5	1	4

Picture Subtraction: *(page 13)*

3   5   1   5   2   2   4   3

Subtraction Sentences: *(page 14)*

1   3   1   5   1   2

Quick Subtraction Drill: *(page 15)*

5	4	6	4
3	0	4	1
1	2	2	1
4	1	1	

Rocket Ship Math: *(page 16)*

-2	
8	6
9	7
2	0
5	3
7	5
3	1

-3	
9	6
5	2
6	3
8	5
4	1
7	4

-5	
10	5
6	1
9	4
7	2
5	0
8	3

-4	
8	4
6	2
5	1
9	5
7	3
4	0

Float the Boats: *(page 17)*

5	6	2	13	12	
5	5	0	4	18	
1	18	11	4	11	5
6	17	9	17	5	4

Subtraction Sentences: *(page 18)*

8 - 4 = 4	10 - 5 = 5
4 - 1 = 3	3 - 2 = 1
8 - 3 = 5	3 - 2 = 1
6 -3 = 3	6 - 4 = 2

Quick Subtraction Practice: *(page 19)*

7	2	3	4	0
1	8	3	4	3
3	0	5	5	1
0	6	2	2	6
7	7	1	3	0
2	1	4	0	1

Two Digit Subtraction - No Regrouping: *(page 20)*

21	10	2	13	11
11	4	2	12	23
22	23	66	32	52
12	32	30	60	25
12	22	33	34	21
13	22	9	8	6

Two Digit Subtraction - No Regrouping: *(page 21)*

20	18	64	23	40
26	20	33	57	2
56	13	42	4	35
15	52	13	31	32
65	3	22	5	13
57	21	44	60	22

Two Digit Subtraction - With Regrouping: *(page 22)*

5	7	7	5	1
9	9	9	9	5
6	6	10	4	5
9	3	6	6	16
9	8	7	5	6
3	6	9	4	9

Two Digit Subtraction - With Regrouping: *(page 23)*

8	33	7	18	37
49	32	59	7	16
16	48	42	16	17
9	7	49	29	5
56	17	25	13	25
25	8	49	25	46

Two Digit Subtraction - With Regrouping/No Regrouping: *(page 24)*

9	20	7	3	67
9	43	66	19	21
8	9	22	25	13
8	60	9	52	9
23	30	18	30	9
7	23	21	31	9

Word Problems: *(page 25)*

12 - 5 = 7   17 - 8 = 9
27 - 13 = 14   6 - 4 = 2
22 - 6 = 16   48 - 39 = 9

Two Digit Subtraction - With Regrouping/No Regrouping: *(page 26)*

40	17	68	8	42
26	43	37	45	60
17	25	20	18	29
59	46	19	45	33
75	53	29	36	9
28	43	13	24	12

Word Problems: *(page 27)*

7 - 4 = 3   12 - 5 = 7
27 - 12 = 15

Two Digit Subtraction: *(page 28)*

34	21	37	33	12
22	32	13	33	66
25	21	31	33	41
51	21	33	30	20
44	47	27	23	21
34	12	35	35	25

Word Problems: *(page 29)*

109 - 89 = 20
876 - 342 = 534
117 - 64 = 53
120 - 73 = 47

More Rocket Math: *(page 30)*

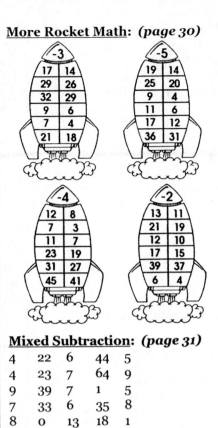

Mixed Subtraction: *(page 31)*

4	22	6	44	5
4	23	7	64	9
9	39	7	1	5
7	33	6	35	8
8	0	13	18	1
10	21	7	32	5

Subtraction Wheels: *(page 32)*

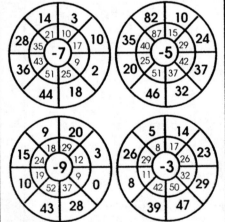

Subtraction - More Practice: *(page 33)*

32	26	15	59	18
17	29	27	39	38
23	11	52	11	33
25	1	43	11	15
51	7	17	33	58
66	35	49	32	15

Bubble Subtraction: *(page 34)*

6	8	18	22	5	19
25	16	16	5	18	16

Three Digit Subtraction - No Regrouping: *(page 35)*

231	80	139	845	40
553	124	10	52	111
413	241	443	443	332
31	253	25	504	348
13	521	144	621	606
464	265	185	43	301

Three Digit Subtraction - No Regrouping: *(page 36)*

20	341	303	660	52
302	162	32	345	602
61	725	325	570	516
623	562	241	203	111
55	513	50	11	11

Three Digit Subtraction - With Regrouping: *(page 37)*

27	71	187	42	128
349	217	31	47	222
147	584	177	727	144
188	99	88	459	533
395	582	83	269	450

What's Missing?: *(page 38)*

(53, 22)	47	(48, 37)	(31, 51)
25	16	(66, 33)	84
25	52	11	26
10	(94, 82)	46	22
53	63	(36, 15)	16

You're a Star!: *(page 39)*

6	10	28
24	33	43
21	23	25
5	7	32
48	28	61

Grocery Bag Subtraction: *(page 40)*

Answers may vary as long as the equations equal the answers.

Word Problems: *(page 41)*

5294 - 3207 = 2087
39 - 14 = 25
480 - 27 = 453
42 - 19 = 23

Mixed Subtraction - No Regrouping: *(page 42)*

5	3	44	250	47
605	51	2	142	32
716	26	13	25	503
186	24	20	274	71
44	4	23	1	2
240	54	70	2	421

Mixed Subtraction - No Regrouping: *(page 43)*

83	32	566	65	2
32	21	21	131	3
210	7	400	44	405
17	118	22	319	68
37	61	204	10	631
2	16	6	141	3

Banner Subtraction: *(page 44)*

13	13	53	55
70	13	6	21
11	12	21	50
28	33	24	33

Subtraction with Decmials -
With Regrouping/No Regrouping: *(page 45)*

1.55	1.85	2.22	0.25	0.62
4.28	7.33	0.15	2.94	1.1
0.44	4.22	8.12	0.82	2.34
4.07	2.47	2.24	0.78	3.49
0.27	1.39	1.47	0.19	2.72
7.30	3.07	1.00	8.01	1.23

Subtraction with Decimals -
With Regrouping/no Regrouping: *(page 46)*

70.60	20.50	81.77	61.96
0.07	0.37	0.60	6.93
33.12	1.08	63.23	22.23
1.45	5.01	1.60	3.16
1.44	8.04	2.03	22.06

Subtraction Review - One and
Two Digit Numbers: *(page 47)*

54	8	6	4	4
18	10	39	3	2
52	4	70	28	58
1	10	40	40	31
77	4	1	31	9
49	36	8	13	51

Subtraction Review - One and
Two Digit Numbers: *(page 48)*

11	57	25	20	71
35	24	1	63	6
14	16	50	90	11
62	16	9	43	1
78	7	23	24	19
13	12	65	38	55

Subtraction Review - Two and Three Digit Numbers: *(page 49)*

177	210	54	6	358
670	385	255	4	286
20	981	4	7	18
37	10	756	39	3
423	52	111	70	130
4	483	28	59	58

Mixed Review: *(page 50)*

6	0.25	28	8	23
15	443	24	0.01	1.46
4.33	0.05	245	2	26.71
30.03	6	4	451	41
1	0.12	10	29	1.60
37	550	3.16	10	13

Two Digit Subtraction: *(page 51)*

37	42	55	84	29
5	12	13	6	56
1	34	45	44	2
50	5	39	13	1
6	52	8	57	34
9	50	25	7	9

Three Digit Subtraction: *(page 52)*

394	903	173	407	738
172	401	107	14	151
211	503	25	197	772
315	543	269	469	87
10	118	46	3	120
197	55	554	328	34

Word Problems: *(page 53)*

12 - 4 = 8
13 - 3 = 10
8 - 6 = 2

Mixed Subtraction: *(page 54)*

271	45	116	119	44
29	63	245	7	110
45	107	35	98	24
44	742	16	412	1
388	17	11	199	38

Subtraction Wheels: *(page 55)*

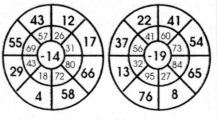

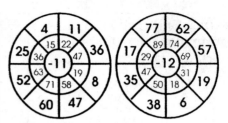

Subtracting Decimals: *(page 56)*

12.98	0.21	28.60	0.54	4.47
7.86	66.46	2.53	2.31	0.61
51.26	3.20	48.48	3.06	2.79
1.36	39.44	2.09	12.11	0.43
52.57	4.59	13.20	4.98	81.83

Word Problems: *(page 57)*

3 - 1 = 2
431 - 138 = 293
93 - 77 = 16

The Sky's the Limit: *(page 58)*

25	163	1
144	19	7
229	42	23

Four Digit Subtraction - With Regrouping/No Regrouping: *(page 59)*

3572	4181	1592	2163
1732	6488	3642	2201
1383	2319	2302	3720
986	6236	3464	1122
1540	3041	4025	2480
1837	3006	6288	2529

Decimal Subtraction Review: *(page 60)*

0.78	1.99	6.53	0.29	1.42
0.21	1.50	35.95	1.14	0.19
0.19	3.06	0.23	3.34	1.33
6.57	64.16	0.05	1.42	0.26
32.66	7.29	4.11	0.04	1.32
0.27	1.64	3.83	2.79	0.12

Publication Listing

Code #	Title and Grade
SSN1-27	Unicorns in Literature Gr. 3-5
SSJ1-44	Upper & Lower Canada Gr. 7-8
SSN1-192	Using Novels Canadian North Gr. 7-8
SSC1-14	Valentines Day Gr. 5-8
SSPC-45	Vegetables B/W Pictures
SSY1-01	Very Hungry Caterpillar NS 30/Pkg Gr. 1-3
SSF1-13	Victorian Era Gr. 7-8
SSC1-35	Victorian Christmas Gr. 5-8
SSF1-17	Viking Age Gr. 4-6
SSN1-206	War with Grandpa SN Gr. 4-6
SSB1-91	Water Gr. 2-4
SSN1-166	Watership Down NS Gr. 7-8
SSH1-16	Ways We Travel Gr. P-K
SSN1-101	Wayside Sch. Little Stranger NS Gr. 4-6
SSN1-76	Wayside Sch. is Falling Down NS 4-6
SSB1-60	Weather Gr. 4-6
SSN1-17	Wee Folk in Literature Gr. 3-5
SSPC-08	Weeds B/W Pictures
SSQ1-04	Welcome Back – Big Book Pkg 1-3
SSB1-73	Whale Preservation Gr. 5-8
SSH1-08	What is a Community? Gr. 2-4
SSH1-01	What is a Family? Gr. 2-3
SSH1-09	What is a School? Gr. 1-2
SSJ1-32	What is Canada? Gr. P-K
SSN1-79	What is RAD? Read & Discover 2-4
SSB1-62	What is the Weather Today? Gr. 2-4
SSN1-194	What's a Daring Detective NS 4-6
SSH1-10	What's My Number Gr. P-K
SSR1-02	What's the Scoop on Words Gr. 4-6
SSN1-73	Where the Red Fern Grows NS Gr. 7-8
SSN1-87	Where the Wild Things Are NS Gr. 1-3
SSN1-187	Whipping Boy NS Gr. 4-6
SSN1-226	Who is Frances Rain? NS Gr. 4-6
SSN1-74	Who's Got Gertie & How...? NS Gr. 4-6
SSN1-131	Why did the Underwear ... NS 4-6
SSC1-28	Why Wear a Poppy? Gr. 2-3
SSJ1-11	Wild Animals of Canada Gr. 2-3
SSPC-07	Wild Flowers B/W Pictures
SSB1-18	Winter Birds Gr. 2-3
SSZ1-03	Winter Olympics Gr. 4-6
SSM1-04	Winter Wonderland Gr. 1
SSC1-01	Witches Gr. 3-4
SSN1-213	Wolf Island NS Gr. 1-3
SSE1-09	Wolfgang Amadeus Mozart 6-9
SSB1-23	Wolves Gr. 3-5
SSC1-20	Wonders of Easter Gr. 2
SSY1-15	Word Families Gr. 1-3
SSR1-59	Word Families 2,3 Letter Words Gr. 1-3
SSR1-60	Word Families 3, 4 Letter Words Gr. 1-3
SSR1-61	Word Families 2, 3, 4 Letter Words Big Book Gr. 1-3
SSB1-35	World of Horses Gr. 4-6
SSB1-13	World of Pets Gr. 2-3
SSF1-26	World War II Gr. 7-8
SSN1-221	Wrinkle in Time NS Gr. 7-8
SSPC-02	Zoo Animals B/W Pictures
SSB1-08	Zoo Animals Gr. 1-2
SSB1-09	Zoo Celebration Gr. 3-4